Eureka Math®
Grade 1
Module 3

Special thanks go to the Gordon A. Cain Center and to the Department of Mathematics at Louisiana State University for their support in the development of *Eureka Math*.

For a free *Eureka Math* Teacher
Resource Pack, Parent Tip
Sheets, and more please visit
https://eurekamath.greatminds.org/teacher-resource-pack

Published by the Great Minds

Copyright © 2015 Great Minds®. No part of this work may be reproduced, sold, or commercialized, in whole or in part, without written permission from Great Minds. Non-commercial use is licensed pursuant to a Creative Commons Attribution-NonCommercial-ShareAlike 4.0 license; for more information, go to http://greatminds.net/maps/math/copyright. "Great Minds" and "Eureka Math" are registered trademarks of Great Minds.

Printed in the U.S.A.

This book may be purchased from the publisher at eureka-math.org

BAB 10 9 8 7 6 5 4 3 2

ISBN 978-1-63255-350-8

Eureka Math: A Story of Units® Contributors

Katrina Abdussalaam, Curriculum Writer
Tiah Alphonso, Program Manager—Curriculum Production
Kelly Alsup, Lead Writer / Editor, Grade 4
Catriona Anderson, Program Manager—Implementation Support
Debbie Andorka-Aceves, Curriculum Writer
Eric Angel, Curriculum Writer
Leslie Arceneaux, Lead Writer / Editor, Grade 5
Kate McGill Austin, Lead Writer / Editor, Grades PreK–K
Adam Baker, Lead Writer / Editor, Grade 5
Scott Baldridge, Lead Mathematician and Lead Curriculum Writer
Beth Barnes, Curriculum Writer
Bonnie Bergstresser, Math Auditor
Bill Davidson, Fluency Specialist
Jill Diniz, Program Director
Nancy Diorio, Curriculum Writer
Nancy Doorey, Assessment Advisor
Lacy Endo-Peery, Lead Writer / Editor, Grades PreK–K
Ana Estela, Curriculum Writer
Lessa Faltermann, Math Auditor
Janice Fan, Curriculum Writer
Ellen Fort, Math Auditor
Peggy Golden, Curriculum Writer
Maria Gomes, Pre-Kindergarten Practitioner
Pam Goodner, Curriculum Writer
Greg Gorman, Curriculum Writer
Melanie Gutierrez, Curriculum Writer
Bob Hollister, Math Auditor
Kelley Isinger, Curriculum Writer
Nuhad Jamal, Curriculum Writer
Mary Jones, Lead Writer / Editor, Grade 4
Halle Kananak, Curriculum Writer
Susan Lee, Lead Writer / Editor, Grade 3
Jennifer Loftin, Program Manager—Professional Development
Soo Jin Lu, Curriculum Writer
Nell McAnelly, Project Director

Table of Contents

GRADE 1 • MODULE 3

Ordering and Comparing Length Measurements as Numbers

© 2015 Great Minds. eureka-math.org
G1-M3-TE-BK3-1.3.1-01.2016

Grade 1 • Module 3

Ordering and Comparing Length Measurements as Numbers

OVERVIEW

Grade 1 Module 3 opens in Topic A by extending students' Kindergarten experiences with direct length comparison to the new learning of indirect comparison whereby the length of one object is used to compare the lengths of two other objects (**1.MD.1**). "My string is longer than your book. Your book is longer than my pencil. That means my string is longer than my pencil!" Students use the same transitivity, or indirect comparison, to compare short distances within the classroom in order to find the shortest path to their classroom door, which is helpful to know for lining up and for emergencies. Students place one endpoint of a length of string at their desks and then extend the string toward the door to see if it will reach. After using the same piece of string from two students' desks, they make statements such as, "Maya's path is shorter than the string. Bailey's path is longer than the string. That means Bailey's path to the door is longer than Maya's path."

EUREKA MATH

Topic B takes *longer than* and *shorter than* to a new level of precision by introducing the idea of a *length unit*. Centimeter cubes are laid alongside the length of an object as students learn that the total number of cubes laid end to end with no gaps or overlaps represents the length of that object (**1.MD.2**). The Geometric Measurement Progressions Document expresses the research indicating the importance of teaching standard units to Grade 1 students *before* non-standard units. Thus, Grade 1 students learn about the centimeter before exploring non-standard units of measurement in this module. Simply lining the cubes up to the ruler allows students to see that they are using units, which relate to a tool used around the world. One of the primary reasons why we recognize standard units is because they are ubiquitous, used on rulers at Grandma's house in the Bronx, in school, and in local shops. Students ask and answer the question, "Why would we use a standard unit to measure?" The topic closes with students measuring and comparing sets of three items using centimeter cubes. They return to the statements of Topic A, but now with more sophisticated insights, such as "The pencil measures 10 centimeters. The crayon measures 6 centimeters. The book measures 20 centimeters. I can put them in order from shortest to longest: the crayon, the pencil, the book. The book is longer than the pencil, and the pencil is longer than the crayon, so the book is longer than the crayon" (**1.MD.1**).

Topic C explores the usefulness of measuring with similar units. Students measure the same objects from Topic B using two different non-standard units, toothpicks and small paper clips, simultaneously to measure one object and answer the question, "Why do we measure with same-sized length units?" (**1.MD.2**). They realize that using iterations of the *same* unit will yield consistent measurement results. Similarly, students explore what it means to use a different unit of measurement from their classmates. It becomes obvious to students that if we want to have discussions about the lengths of objects, we *must* measure with the same units. Students answer the question, "If Bailey uses paper clips and Maya uses toothpicks, and they both measure things in our classroom, will they be able to compare their measurements?" With this new understanding of consistent measurement, Topic C closes with students solving *compare with difference unknown* problems. Students use standard units to answer such questions as, "How much longer is the pencil than the marker?" (**1.OA.1**).

Topic D closes the module as students represent and interpret data (**1.MD.4**). They collect data about their classmates and sort that information into three categories. Using same-sized pictures on squares, students represent this sorted data so that it can be easily compared and described. Students interpret information presented in the graphs by first determining the number of data points in a given category, for example, "How many students like carrots the best?" Then, students combine categories, for example, "How many total students like carrots or broccoli the best?" The module closes with students asking and answering varied questions about data sets, such as "How many students were polled in all?" (*put together with result unknown*) and "How many more students preferred broccoli to string beans?" (*compare with difference unknown*) (**1.OA.1**). Their work with units representing data points is an application of students' earlier work with length as they observe that each square can be lightly interpreted as a length unit, which helps them analyze the data.

Notes on Pacing for Differentiation

Students need Module 3's fluency before advancing to Module 4. In the event that there are critical pacing issues, consider moving Topic D (Lessons 10–13, focusing on graphing and data interpretation) to another time in the day (e.g., science, morning routine).

Note that Lessons 2, 4, 6, and 9 are the most essential lessons of Module 3.

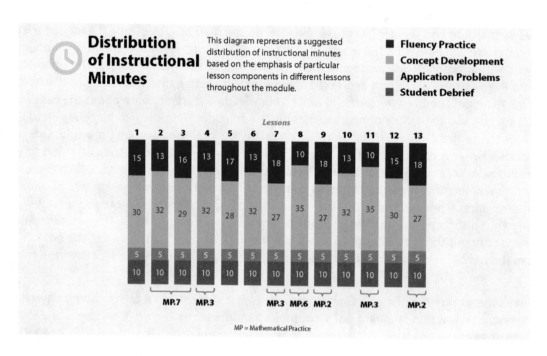

Focus Grade Level Standards

Represent and solve problems involving addition and subtraction.[1]

1.OA.1 Use addition and subtraction within 20 to solve word problems involving situations of adding to, taking from, putting together, taking apart, and comparing, with unknowns in all positions, e.g., by using objects, drawings, and equations with a symbol for the unknown number to represent the problem.

Measure lengths indirectly and by iterating length units.

1.MD.1 Order three objects by length; compare the lengths of two objects indirectly by using a third object.

1.MD.2 Express the length of an object as a whole number of length units, by laying multiple copies of a shorter object (the length unit) end to end; understand that the length measurement of an object is the number of same-size length units that span it with no gaps or overlaps. *Limit to contexts where the object being measured is spanned by a whole number of length units with no gaps or overlaps.*

Represent and interpret data.

1.MD.4 Organize, represent, and interpret data with up to three categories; ask and answer questions about the total number of data points, how many in each category, and how many more or less are in one category than in another.

---

[1]The balance of this cluster is addressed in Module 2.

EUREKA
MATH

Foundational Standards

K.CC.5 Count to answer "how many?" questions about as many as 20 things arranged in a line, a rectangular array, or a circle, or as many as 10 things in a scattered configuration; given a number from 1–20, count out that many objects.

K.CC.6 Identify whether the number of objects in one group is greater than, less than, or equal to the number of objects in another group, e.g., by using matching and counting strategies. (Include groups with up to ten objects.)

K.CC.7 Compare two numbers between 1 and 10 presented as written numerals.

K.MD.1 Describe measurable attributes of objects, such as length or weight. Describe several measurable attributes of a single object.

K.MD.2 Directly compare two objects with a measurable attribute in common, to see which object has "more of"/"less of" the attribute, and describe the difference. *For example, directly compare the heights of two children and describe one child as taller/shorter.*

Focus Standards for Mathematical Practice

MP.2 **Reason quantitatively and abstractly.** Students describe and compare lengths using *longer than* and *shorter than* and numerically represent relationships among and between lengths. This takes place in the context of comparing sets within data collection as well as comparing objects with different length units. For example, students compare the number of peers who enjoy one hobby with the number of peers who enjoy a different hobby. Students also compare the length of one object, in centimeter cubes, with the length of a second object, in centimeter cubes.

MP.3 **Construct viable arguments and critique the reasoning of others.** Students describe and explain their process of finding accurate length measurements and challenge each other to measure precisely.

MP.6 **Attend to precision.** Students use measuring tools, such as centimeter cubes, precisely and explain precisely the cause of errors in using the tools.

MP.7 **Look for and make use of structure.** Students use transitivity to compare multiple objects. "My string is longer than the pencil. My string is shorter than the book. That means the book is longer than the pencil." In this case, students use the string as the structure to compare the book and the pencil.

Overview of Module Topics and Lesson Objectives

Standards		Topics and Objectives	Days
1.MD.1	A	**Indirect Comparison in Length Measurement**	3
		Lesson 1: Compare length directly and consider the importance of aligning endpoints.	
		Lesson 2: Compare length using indirect comparison by finding objects *longer than, shorter than,* and *equal in length to* that of a string.	
		Lesson 3: Order three lengths using indirect comparison.	
1.MD.1 1.MD.2	B	**Standard Length Units**	3
		Lesson 4: Express the length of an object using centimeter cubes as length units to measure with no gaps or overlaps.	
		Lesson 5: Rename and measure with centimeter cubes, using their standard unit name of centimeters.	
		Lesson 6: Order, measure, and compare the length of objects before and after measuring with centimeter cubes, solving *compare with difference unknown* word problems.	
1.OA.1 1.MD.2	C	**Non-Standard and Standard Length Units**	3
		Lesson 7: Measure the same objects from Topic B with different non-standard units simultaneously to see the need to measure with a consistent unit.	
		Lesson 8: Understand the need to use the same units when comparing measurements with others.	
		Lesson 9: Answer *compare with difference unknown* problems about lengths of two different objects measured in centimeters.	
1.OA.1 1.MD.4	D	**Data Interpretation**	4
		Lessons 10–11: Collect, sort, and organize data; then ask and answer questions about the number of data points.	
		Lessons 12–13: Ask and answer varied word problem types about a data set with three categories.	
		End-of-Module Assessment: Topics A–D (assessment ½ day, return ½ day, remediation or further applications 1 day)	2
Total Number of Instructional Days			15

EUREKA MATH

Terminology

New or Recently Introduced Terms

- Centimeter (standard length unit within the metric system)
- Centimeter cube (pictured to the right, also used as a length unit in this module)
- Centimeter ruler (measurement tool using length units of centimeters)
- Data (collected information)
- Endpoint (the end of an object, referenced when aligning for measurement purposes)
- Height (measurement of vertical distance of an object)
- Length unit (measuring the length of an object with equal-sized units)
- Poll (survey)
- Table or graph (organized charts visually representing data)

Familiar Terms and Symbols[2]

- Less than
- Longer than/taller than
- More than
- Shorter than
- Tally marks

Suggested Tools and Representations

- Centimeter cubes
- Centimeter rulers (simply for the purpose of naming the centimeter)
- Non-standard units (toothpicks, small and large paper clips)
- String lengths of about 25 centimeters
- Tally marks

Homework

Homework at the K–1 level is not a convention in all schools. In this curriculum, homework is an opportunity for additional practice of the content from the day's lesson. The teacher is encouraged, with the support of parents, administrators, and colleagues, to discern the appropriate use of homework for his or her students. Fluency exercises can also be considered as an alternative homework assignment.

---

[2]These are terms and symbols students have seen previously.

Scaffolds[3]

The scaffolds integrated into *A Story of Units*® give alternatives for how students access information as well as express and demonstrate their learning. Strategically placed margin notes are provided within each lesson elaborating on the use of specific scaffolds at applicable times. They address many needs presented by English language learners, students with disabilities, students performing above grade level, and students performing below grade level. Many of the suggestions are organized by Universal Design for Learning (UDL) principles and are applicable to more than one population. To read more about the approach to differentiated instruction in *A Story of Units,* please refer to "How to Implement *A Story of Units.*"

Assessment Summary

Type	Administered	Format	Standards Addressed
End-of-Module Assessment Task	After Topic D	Constructed response with rubric	1.OA.1 1.MD.1 1.MD.2 1.MD.4

---

[3]Students with disabilities may require Braille, large print, audio, or special digital files. Please visit the website www.p12.nysed.gov/specialed/aim for specific information on how to obtain student materials that satisfy the National Instructional Materials Accessibility Standard (NIMAS) format.

EUREKA MATH™

Mathematics Curriculum

Topic A

Indirect Comparison in Length Measurement

1.MD.1

Focus Standard:	1.MD.1	Order three objects by length; compare the lengths of two objects indirectly by using a third object.
Instructional Days:	3	
Coherence -Links from:	GK–M3	Comparison of Length, Weight, Capacity, and Numbers to 10
-Links to:	G2–M2	Addition and Subtraction of Length Units
	G2–M7	Problem Solving with Length, Money, and Data

The module opens in Topic A by extending students' Kindergarten experiences with direct length measurement to indirect measurement whereby the length of one object is used to compare that of two other objects (**1.MD.1**).

Students explore direct comparison in Lesson 1, comparing the length of two objects by paying close attention to the endpoints of each to ensure accurate comparisons. Students draw on their Kindergarten experiences as they use *longer than* and *shorter than* as they compare.

In Lesson 2, students begin to use indirect comparison (or transitivity) as they compare each item to one consistent item, such as a piece of string or a strip of construction paper of a specific length. Items are then compared to each other through indirect comparison. For instance, if the crayon is shorter than the paper strip, and the pencil is longer than the paper strip, we can say that the crayon is also shorter than the pencil. As a way to prove their conclusions from indirect comparisons, students use direct comparison to verify their claims.

Lesson 3 extends the use of indirect comparison to compare distances between objects that cannot be moved next to each other for direct comparison. Students use the same transitive process to compare short distances within the classroom in order to find the shortest path to their classroom door, which is helpful to know for lining up and for emergencies. After measuring each path from their desks to the door with the same piece of string, students are able to make statements, such as "Maya's path is shorter than the string. Bailey's path is longer than the string. That means Bailey's path to the door is longer than Maya's path." Using grid lines on classroom floor tiles and on provided maps of city blocks, students compare distances of various paths.

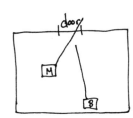

A Teaching Sequence Toward Mastery of Indirect Comparison in Length Measurement

Objective 1: Compare length directly and consider the importance of aligning endpoints.
(Lesson 1)

Objective 2: Compare length using indirect comparison by finding objects *longer than, shorter than,* and *equal in length to* that of a string.
(Lesson 2)

Objective 3: Order three lengths using indirect comparison.
(Lesson 3)

© 2015 Great Minds. eureka-math.org
G1-M3-TE-BK3-1.3.1-01.2016

Lesson 1

Objective: Compare length directly and consider the importance of aligning endpoints.

Suggested Lesson Structure

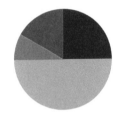

■ Fluency Practice   (15 minutes)
■ Application Problem   (5 minutes)
■ Concept Development (30 minutes)
■ Student Debrief   (10 minutes)
  Total Time   **(60 minutes)**

Fluency Practice (15 minutes)

- Speed Writing **1.NBT.1**   (2 minutes)
- Tens and Ones **1.NBT.2**   (3 minutes)
- Sprint: Subtracting Ones from Teen Numbers **1.OA.6**   (10 minutes)

Speed Writing (2 minutes)

Materials: (S) Personal white board

Note: This fluency activity provides students practice with writing numbers while reinforcing place value understanding.

Tell students to write their numbers from 10 to as high as they can in one minute while they whisper count the Say Ten way. Teachers may also want to instruct students to organize their numbers in a column so that the patterns in the tens and ones columns become visible.

Tens and Ones (3 minutes)

Materials: (T) 100-bead Rekenrek

Note: This activity addresses the Grade 1 standard requiring students to understand that two-digit numbers represent amounts of tens and ones.

Practice decomposing numbers into tens and ones using the Rekenrek.

    T: (Show 16 on the Rekenrek.) How many tens do you see?
    S: 1.
    T: How many ones?
    S: 6.

T: Say the number the Say Ten way.

S: Ten 6.

T: Good. 1 ten plus 6 ones is…?

S: 16.

T: (Slide over 10 from the next row.) How many tens do you see?

S: 2.

T: How many ones?

S: 6.

T: Say the number the Say Ten way.

S: 2 tens 6.

T: Good. 2 tens plus 6 ones is…?

S: 26.

Slide over the next row and repeat. Continue with the following suggested sequence within 40: 15, 25, 35; 17, 27, 37; and 19, 29, 39.

Sprint: Subtracting Ones from Teen Numbers (10 minutes)

Materials: (S) Subtracting Ones from Teen Numbers Sprint

Note: This Sprint addresses the Grade 1 standard of adding and subtracting within 20 and provides continued practice from the lessons at the end of Module 2.

Application Problem (5 minutes)

Nigel and Corey each have new pencils that are the same length. Corey uses his pencil so much that he needs to sharpen it several times. Nigel doesn't use his at all. Nigel and Corey compare pencils. Whose pencil is longer? Draw a picture to show your thinking.

Note: In this Application Problem, students use their prior experiences to consider what happens to a pencil after repeated use and then use that knowledge to compare a new with a used pencil. Students have the opportunity to draw to show their understanding of length and of the term *longer*. During the Student Debrief, students discuss drawings in light of today's lesson, making statements such as, "Corey's pencil is shorter than Nigel's pencil. Nigel's pencil is longer than Corey's pencil."

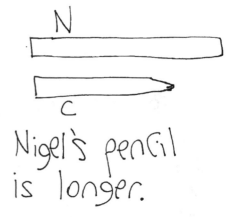

Concept Development (30 minutes)

Materials: (T) Folder, new crayon, pencil, dry erase marker, jumbo glue stick, *longer than* and *shorter than* sentence frames (Template) (S) Folder, 5 strips of paper (of varying lengths) per pair, various classroom objects

Have students sit in a meeting area in a semicircle.

T: (Prop up a folder on the floor. Hold a dry erase marker and a pencil behind the folder, making the marker appear taller than the pencil.) Which of these items, the marker or the pencil, is longer?

S: The marker!

T: How do you know?

S: The marker is taller. → The pencil is shorter.

T: (Call up a student.) Please take away the folder and reveal what's behind it.

S: (Takes away the folder.)

T: (Keep the way the marker and the pencil were held.) Now, can you tell which one is longer? Turn and talk to your partner.

S: The marker is longer because the top of it is taller. → The pencil is taller. Look at how much higher up the marker is in the air. → It's hard to tell.

T: (Stand both items on the floor, side by side.) Now, can you tell which one is longer?

S: Yes! The pencil is longer!

T: (Project the sentence frame with *longer than* from the Template.) Which is longer? Use this sentence frame to say your answer.

S: The pencil is *longer than* the marker.

T: (Project the sentence frame with *shorter than*.) Which is shorter? Use this sentence frame to say your answer.

S: The marker is shorter than the pencil.

T: Are you sure about your answer?

S: Yes.

T: Turn and talk to your partner about what I did differently to help you be sure that the pencil is longer than the marker.

S: You put both things on the floor. → They started at the same place.

T: So, what do we have to make sure to do when we compare two different objects to see which is longer?

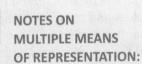

NOTES ON MULTIPLE MEANS OF REPRESENTATION:

Highlight the critical vocabulary for English language learners by showing a visual representation of new words. Vocabulary that should be highlighted includes *shorter than, longer than,* and *endpoint.* Without understanding these words, English language learners may have difficulty with this module.

EUREKA MATH

Lesson 1: Compare length directly and consider the importance of aligning endpoints.

13

© 2015 Great Minds. eureka-math.org
G1-M3-TE-BK3-1.3.1-01.2016

S: You have to start at the same spot. That's the fair way to see which is longer.

T: You're right. We have to pay close attention and make sure we line up the very end of each object, which we call the **endpoint**, so that we can accurately compare which is longer or shorter.

T: Let's try it again. (Hold up the crayon in the other hand in a fist and the jumbo glue stick in the other fist, making the crayon appear longer.) Which is longer? Turn and talk to your partner.

S: The crayon. → No. We can't tell. We don't know if they are starting from the same place.

T: Good thinking! You can't be sure which is longer because I'm hiding the endpoints. Turn and talk to your partner about how you would arrange these items so we can accurately figure out which is longer.

Students discuss as the teacher circulates to choose a volunteer with the idea of aligning the endpoints.

T: (Call up a student to demonstrate.) What did he do to make sure we can be accurate about which item is longer?

S: He lined up the endpoints!

T: Which is longer, the crayon or the glue stick? Use the sentence frame to say your answer.

S: The glue stick is longer than the crayon.

Allow students to "fool" their friends with varying endpoints. Pass out the paper strips and folders. Partner A hides behind the folder and selects two paper strips. She holds them up, and Partner B guesses which one is longer. Partner A can then reveal the actual lengths. Students should discuss Partner B's guess and why it was accurate or inaccurate. After discussion, they can switch roles.

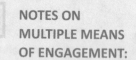

NOTES ON MULTIPLE MEANS OF ENGAGEMENT:

Students may need some extra practice understanding how to compare lengths of different objects accurately. Help them to understand the importance of endpoints. Offer opportunities for student leadership as "teacher" for those students who understand the concept of an endpoint.

T: Now that we know about endpoints, let's practice lining things up! Go on a scavenger hunt. Find two items of different lengths, one longer or shorter than the other. You have one minute to bring those items to your table.

Students look around the room to find two items of different lengths.

T: Show how you can compare the length of your two items. Then, make two statements to your partner using the sentence frames.

T: I saw you making sure to line up your items. Now try this: Flip just one of your items, and make it stand upside down. Does this change which item is longer or shorter?

S: (Flip and compare.) No.

T: Why not?

S: Because it doesn't matter if you have them standing the regular way or upside down as long as you line up the endpoints.

Lesson 1:   Compare length directly and consider the importance of aligning endpoints.

© 2015 Great Minds. eureka-math.org
G1-M3-TE-BK3-1.3.1-01.2016

T: I observed so many students lining up their endpoints by making them stand from the table. Can you show a different way to line up the endpoints? (Have students share the different ways in which they can align the endpoints.)

S: You can lay them down, one on top of the other. Just make sure the endpoints are starting at the same line. → You can use the edge of the table and lay down the items so they both start from the same place.

If time allows, give students several one-minute periods to look for more objects and practice comparing lengths by aligning endpoints and making accurate statements.

Problem Set (8 minutes)

Students should do their personal best to complete the Problem Set within the allotted 8 minutes. Some problems do not specify a method for solving. This is an intentional reduction of scaffolding that invokes MP.5, Use Appropriate Tools Strategically. Students should solve these problems using the RDW approach used for Application Problems.

For some classes, it may be appropriate to modify the assignment by specifying which problems students should work on first. With this option, let the purposeful sequencing of the Problem Set guide your selections so that problems continue to be scaffolded. Balance word problems with other problem types to ensure a range of practice. Consider assigning incomplete problems for homework or at another time during the day.

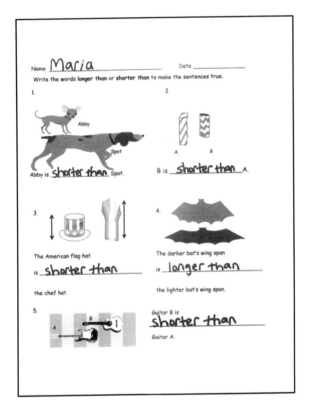

Student Debrief (10 minutes)

Lesson Objective: Compare length directly and consider the importance of aligning endpoints.

The Student Debrief is intended to invite reflection and active processing of the total lesson experience.

Invite students to review their solutions for the Problem Set. They should check work by comparing answers with a partner before going over answers as a class. Look for misconceptions or misunderstandings that can be addressed in the Debrief. Guide students in a conversation to debrief the Problem Set and process the lesson.

Any combination of the questions below may be used to lead the discussion.

- When we compare lengths of different objects, what do we need to do to make sure we are comparing accurately?
- When you compare two objects and see that one of them is longer, can you make an accurate statement about which is shorter without looking? How?

Lesson 1:   Compare length directly and consider the importance of aligning endpoints.

© 2015 Great Minds. eureka-math.org
G1-M3-TE-BK3-1.3.1-01.2016

15

- I saw one student compare the length of two objects by standing both objects on the table instead of standing the objects on the floor. Will the student be able to compare them accurately? Why or why not?

- Look at the bats in Problem 4. Were the **endpoints** aligned? Could you still see which bat has the longer wingspan? How?

- Look at the pencils and bones from Problems 6 and 7. Compare a pencil to a bone, and talk about how they are longer or shorter than one nother and how you know.

- Look at your drawings from today's Application Problem. Do your drawings show an accurate way to compare the length of these two pencils? If not, redraw your solution based on what you now know about endpoints.

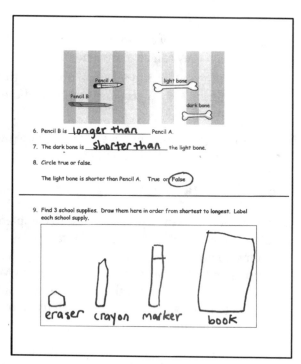

6. Pencil B is _longer than_ Pencil A.

7. The dark bone is _shorter than_ the light bone.

8. Circle true or false.

   The light bone is shorter than Pencil A.   True or False

9. Find 3 school supplies. Draw them here in order from shortest to longest. Label each school supply.

eraser   crayon   marker   book

Exit Ticket (3 minutes)

After the Student Debrief, instruct students to complete the Exit Ticket. A review of their work will help with assessing students' understanding of the concepts that were presented in today's lesson and planning more effectively for future lessons. The questions may be read aloud to the students.

Homework

Homework at the K–1 level is not a convention in all schools. In this curriculum, homework is an opportunity for additional practice of the content from the day's lesson. The teacher is encouraged, with the support of parents, administrators, and colleagues, to discern the appropriate use of homework for his or her students. Fluency exercises can also be considered as an alternative homework assignment.

Lesson 1:   Compare length directly and consider the importance of aligning endpoints.

EUREKA MATH

A

Number Correct: _____

Name _____   Date _____

*Write the missing number.

1.	$3 - 3 = \square$		16.	$13 - 1 = \square$	
2.	$13 - 3 = \square$		17.	$13 - 2 = \square$	
3.	$3 - 2 = \square$		18.	$14 - 3 = \square$	
4.	$13 - 2 = \square$		19.	$14 - 4 = \square$	
5.	$4 - 2 = \square$		20.	$14 - 10 = \square$	
6.	$14 - 2 = \square$		21.	$17 - 5 = \square$	
7.	$4 - 3 = \square$		22.	$17 - 6 = \square$	
8.	$14 - 3 = \square$		23.	$17 - 10 = \square$	
9.	$14 - 10 = \square$		24.	$8 - \square = 5$	
10.	$7 - 6 = \square$		25.	$18 - \square = 15$	
11.	$17 - 6 = \square$		26.	$18 - \square = 13$	
12.	$17 - 10 = \square$		27.	$19 - \square = 12$	
13.	$6 - 3 = \square$		28.	$\square - 2 = 17$	
14.	$16 - 3 = \square$		29.	$17 - 3 = 16 - \square$	
15.	$16 - 10 = \square$		30.	$19 - 6 = \square - 5$	

EUREKA MATH

Lesson 1:   Compare length directly and consider the importance of aligning endpoints.

© 2015 Great Minds. eureka-math.org
G1-M3-TE-BK3-1.3.1-01.2016

17

B

Name _____

Date _____

*Write the missing number.

1.	2 - 2 = ☐		16.	14 - 1 = ☐	
2.	12 - 2 = ☐		17.	14 - 2 = ☐	
3.	2 - 1 = ☐		18.	15 - 3 = ☐	
4.	12 - 1 = ☐		19.	15 - 4 = ☐	
5.	3 - 3 = ☐		20.	15 - 10 = ☐	
6.	13 - 3 = ☐		21.	18 - 5 = ☐	
7.	3 - 2 = ☐		22.	18 - 6 = ☐	
8.	13 - 2 = ☐		23.	18 - 10 = ☐	
9.	13 - 10 = ☐		24.	7 - ☐ = 5	
10.	6 - 5 = ☐		25.	17 - ☐ = 15	
11.	16 - 5 = ☐		26.	17 - ☐ = 13	
12.	16 - 10 = ☐		27.	19 - ☐ = 13	
13.	4 - 2 = ☐		28.	☐ - 3 = 16	
14.	14 - 2 = ☐		29.	17 - 4 = 16 - ☐	
15.	14 - 10 = ☐		30.	19 - 7 = ☐ - 6	

Lesson 1:   Compare length directly and consider the importance of aligning endpoints.

© 2015 Great Minds. eureka-math.org
G1-M3-TE-BK3-1.3.1-01.2016

EUREKA MATH

Name _____   Date _____

Write the words **longer than** or **shorter than** to make the sentences true.

1.

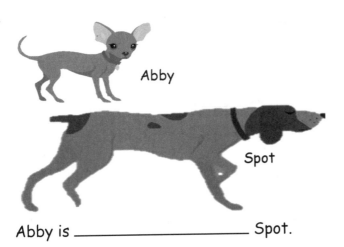

Abby is _____ Spot.

2.

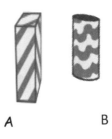

B is _____A.

3.

The American flag hat

is _____

the chef hat.

4.

The darker bat's wingspan

is _____

the lighterer bat's wingspan.

5

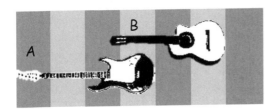

Guitar B is

_____

Guitar A.

Lesson 1:   Compare length directly and consider the importance of aligning endpoints.

19

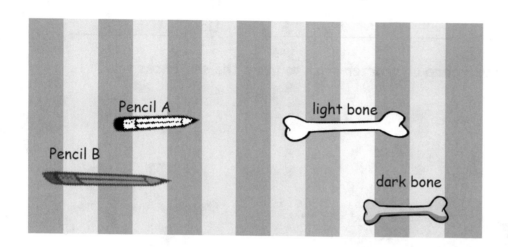

6. Pencil B is _____ Pencil A.

7. The dark bone is _____ the light bone.

8. Circle true or false.
   The light bone is shorter than Pencil A.   **True** or **False**

---

9. Find 3 school supplies. Draw them here in order from **shortest** to **longest**.

   Label each school supply.

Lesson 1: Compare length directly and consider the importance of aligning endpoints.

© 2015 Great Minds. eureka-math.org
G1-M3-TE-BK3-1.3.1-01.2016

EUREKA MATH

Name _____ Date _____

Write the words **longer than** or **shorter than** to make the sentences true.

A

B

Shoe A is _____ Shoe B.

Lesson 1: Compare length directly and consider the importance of aligning endpoints.

© 2015 Great Minds. eureka-math.org
G1-M3-TE-BK3-1.3.1-01.2016

21

Name _____ Date _____

Follow the directions. Complete the sentences.

1. Circle the **longer** rabbit.

Peter

Floppy

_____ is longer than _____ .

2. Circle the **shorter** fruit.

A   B

_____ is shorter than _____ .

Write the words **longer than** or **shorter than** to make the sentences true.

3.

The glue

is _____

the ketchup.

4.

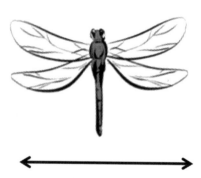

The dragonfly's wingspan

is _____

the butterfly's wingspan.

Lesson 1:   Compare length directly and consider the importance of aligning endpoints.

© 2015 Great Minds. eureka-math.org
G1-M3-TE-BK3-1.3.1-01.2016

EUREKA
MATH

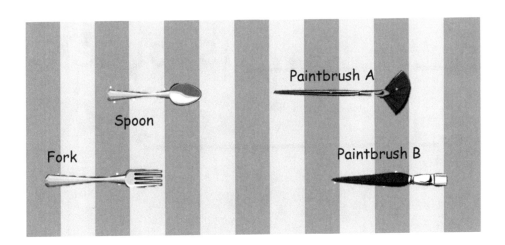

5. Paintbrush A is _____ Paintbrush B.

6. The spoon is _____ the fork.

7. Circle true or false.

   The spoon is shorter than Paintbrush B.   **True** or **False**

___

8. Find 3 objects in your room. Draw them here in order from shortest to longest.
   Label each object.

Lesson 1:   Compare length directly and consider the importance of aligning
             endpoints.

© 2015 Great Minds. eureka-math.org
G1-M3-TE-BK3-1.3.1-01.2016

23

The _____ is longer than the _____.

The _____ is shorter than the _____.

longer than and *shorter than* sentence frames

Lesson 1: Compare length directly and consider the importance of aligning endpoints.

EUREKA MATH

Lesson 2

Objective: Compare length using indirect comparison by finding objects *longer than, shorter than,* and *equal in length to* that of a string.

Suggested Lesson Structure

■ Fluency Practice   (13 minutes)
■ Application Problem   (5 minutes)
■ Concept Development   (32 minutes)
■ Student Debrief   (10 minutes)

Total Time   **(60 minutes)**

Fluency Practice (13 minutes)

- Happy Counting **1.OA.5, 1.NBT.5**   (3 minutes)
- Hide Zero Number Sentences **1.NBT.2, 1.NBT.4**   (3 minutes)
- Addition with Cards **1.NBT.6**   (7 minutes)

Happy Counting (3 minutes)

Note: In the first two modules, students practiced counting by ones, tens, twos, and fives, both the regular way and the Say Ten way. Reviewing these counting patterns within 40 prepares students for Module 4 while strengthening their understanding of place value and their ability to add and subtract.

Choose a counting pattern and range based on the class's skill level. If students are proficient up to 40, star at 40, and quickly go up to 80. If they are proficient between 40 and 80, Happy Count between 80 and 120. To reinforce place value, try alternating between counting the regular way and the Say Ten way.

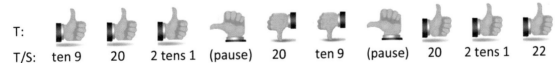

T:

T/S: ten 9   20   2 tens 1   (pause)   20   ten 9   (pause)   20   2 tens 1   22

Hide Zero Number Sentences (3 minutes)

Materials: (S) Hide Zero cards with 0–9 and 10, 20, 30, 40 (Fluency Template 1)

Note: This fluency activity strengthens the understanding of place value and prepares students for Module 4. If students already have Hide Zero cards from previous work, only the final page (10, 20, 30, 40) needs to be copied and distributed.

Show students a number from 10 to 40 with Hide Zero cards (e.g., 15). Students say an addition sentence with 10 as an addend (e.g., 10 + 5 = 15). As students say the sentence, break apart the Hide Zero cards to model the equation. Alternate asking students to say the numbers the Say Ten way and the regular way.

Use the following suggested sequence: 15, 25, 35; 14, 24, 34; and 16, 26, 36.

Addition with Cards (7 minutes)

Materials: (S) Numeral cards 0–10 (Fluency Template 2), counters (if needed)

Note: This review fluency activity strengthens students' abilities to add within and across ten. Numeral cards from previous modules can be used if they have already been produced. Numeral cards 11–15 are needed in later lessons.

Students sit in partnerships. Students shuffle or mix their numeral cards. Each partner places her deck of cards face down. Each partner flips over two cards and adds her cards together. The partner with the greater total keeps the cards played by both players that round. For example Player A draws 4 and 5 and gives the total 9. Player B draws 9 and 4 and gives the total, 13. Since 9<13, Player B keeps the cards. If the sums are equal, the cards are set aside, and the winner of the next round keeps the cards from both rounds. At the end of the game, the players will each be left with 1 card. They each flip their last card over and the player with the highest card says the sum and collects the cards. Students continue to play as time allows.

Application Problem (5 minutes)

Jordan has 3 stuffed animals: a giraffe, a bear, and a monkey. The giraffe is taller than the monkey. The bear is shorter than the monkey. Sketch the animals from shortest to tallest to show how tall each animal is.

Note: This problem directly relates to today's lesson, providing an opportunity to circulate and uncover students' prior understandings and possible misconceptions. Students' drawings should demonstrate the proper alignment of endpoints when they are sketching to show the comparison between the animals. During the Student Debrief, be sure to discuss the use of the terms taller than and longer than when comparing objects. Reinforce the connection between the two terms: that sometimes we describe length in terms of how tall something is when the length is a type of **height**, going from the ground straight up toward the sky.

Lesson 2:   Compare length using indirect comparison by finding objects
             longer than, shorter than, and *equal in length to* that of a string.

EUREKA MATH

Concept Development (32 minutes)

Materials: (T) 2 feet of string, 9 cm long strip of paper, scissors, various classroom objects shorter and longer than the teacher's foot (e.g., board eraser, piece of 9" × 12" construction paper, 8½" × 11" paper on a bulletin board) (S) 1 foot of string, scissors, various classroom objects for measuring length, personal white board with indirect comparison statements (Template), 9 cm long strips (e.g., paper, pipe cleaners, or twist ties)

Have students place their personal white boards at their tables and sit in the meeting area in a semicircle.

T: (Place the string and a strip of paper on the floor for students to see.) I'm looking to see if I can find any items that are longer than or shorter than my foot. Oh, I see one! I really want to compare the length of the paper on the bulletin board to my foot. (Walk over to the bulletin board, and hoist up foot to compare.) Wow. I really want to compare, but it's not easy. What should I do? Talk with your partner to come up with a plan for how I can compare the length of my foot to the length of the paper on the bulletin board. (Answers may vary.)

T: (If students do not mention using a string as a tool to measure the teacher's foot, direct their attention to the activity materials.) Wow. Those were some great ideas! I wonder if using any of these items might also help me. I'm going to get some string and cut it so that it is equal in length to my foot. A string is much easier to use than trying to put my foot against everything I want to compare it to!

T: (Demonstrate measuring foot with a string and cut.) So, this is the same length as...?

S: Your foot!

T: Now, I can walk over to the bulletin board and compare to see if the paper is longer or shorter than my foot. What do I need to do to make sure that we have an accurate comparison?

S: Line up the endpoints!

T: (Align endpoints and measure.) Which is longer, the string or the paper?

S: The paper.

T: So, the paper is longer than the string, and the string is the same length as my foot. So, which is longer, my foot or the paper?

S: The paper is longer than your foot.

T: (Write on the board: The paper is longer than my foot.) I wonder if I can find something that's shorter than my foot. Oh, the white board eraser! Let's check. (Hold up the string.) This string is the same length as...?

S: Your foot.

T: Can I use the string to see if my foot is longer or shorter than the eraser?

S: Yes.

NOTES ON MULTIPLE MEANS OF ACTION AND EXPRESSION:

Some students benefit from extra practice when determining which objects are *longer than, shorter than,* or *equal in length to.* These students may still be trying to comprehend the idea of an endpoint, so the extra practice helps secure their understanding of these terms.

Lesson 2:   Compare length using indirect comparison by finding objects *longer than, shorter than,* and *equal in length to* that of a string.

27

© 2015 Great Minds. eureka-math.org
G1-M3-TE-BK3-1.3.1-01.2016

T: I need to make sure…?

S: The endpoints line up!

T: (Align endpoints and measure.) What do you see?

S: The string is longer than the eraser. → That means your foot is longer than the eraser. → The eraser is shorter than your foot.

T: (Write on the board: The eraser is shorter than my foot.) Great! The string was such an easy way to compare the length of my foot to the length of the other objects. Can we figure out which is longer, the paper or the eraser? Turn and talk to your partner, and explain your thinking.

S: The paper is longer than the eraser.

T: We didn't compare the paper and the eraser by lining them up by their endpoints. How did you know which was longer?

S: The paper was longer than your foot, but the eraser was shorter than your foot, so the paper has to be longer than the eraser!

T: Let's check. (Bring the eraser to the paper on the bulletin board, line up the endpoints, and compare.) You are correct!

T: (Write on the board: The paper is longer than the eraser.) Great thinking!

T: (Hold up a piece of construction paper.) This piece of construction paper is longer than my foot. The paper from the board was longer than my foot, too. Can I tell which type of paper is longer now that I've compared both with my foot? Talk with your partner.

S: (Discuss.) No, you can't tell. → They are both longer, so you don't know which one is the longest. → You would have to have something that's in between the two sizes.

T: That's right. Both the pieces of paper are longer than my foot, but I cannot tell if the construction paper is longer than the paper on the board.

T: Now it's your turn. You'll go on a scavenger hunt to find three items, one that is longer than your foot, one that is shorter than your foot, and lastly, one that is about the same length as your foot. But you won't be able to use your foot to measure! Instead, I will give you a piece of string to use!

MP.7

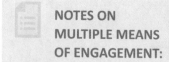

NOTES ON MULTIPLE MEANS OF ENGAGEMENT:

Provide challenging extensions for students who are able to compare length indirectly with a string. Offer them a longer string to use with longer objects, and have them present their findings to the class. Alternatively, students can use their foot length to compare two items that are both longer than their foot, or students can compare objects that are close in length.

Demonstrate how students can work with their partners to measure and cut their piece of string to match their foot (or shoe). Allow five minutes for students to prepare the strings and to look for their items. Have students then return to their seats to fill in their comparison statements on their personal white boards and share their findings with a partner. Have them repeat this process as time allows.

Problem Set (10 minutes)

Students should do their personal best to complete the Problem Set within the allotted 10 minutes. For some classes, it may be appropriate to modify the assignment by specifying which problems they work on first. Some problems do not specify a method for solving. Students should solve these problems using the RDW approach used for Application Problems.

Lesson 2:   Compare length using indirect comparison by finding objects
                                    longer than, shorter than, and *equal in length to* that of a string.

Note: Students use a 9 cm paper strip, pipe cleaner, or twist tie instead of a string to measure each picture in the Problem Set. Explain to students that the paper strip is used in the same fashion as the string, as a measuring tool. Model measuring the first picture (baseball bat) using the paper strip. Prepare today's Problem Set on two separate pieces of paper to avoid having students flip over their papers as they use information from Page 1 to complete Page 2.

Note that students need to take a paper strip home to complete the homework.

Student Debrief (10 minutes)

Lesson Objective: Compare length using indirect comparison by finding objects *longer than, shorter than,* and *equal in length to* that of a string.

The Student Debrief is intended to invite reflection and active processing of the total lesson experience.

Invite students to review their solutions for the Problem Set. They should check work by comparing answers with a partner before going over answers as a class. Look for misconceptions or misunderstandings that can be addressed in the Debrief. Guide students in a conversation to debrief the Problem Set and process the lesson.

Any combination of the questions below may be used to lead the discussion.

- What did we use to compare the length of different objects? (A string and a paper strip.) How were these tools helpful?

- How were you able to figure out the length of different objects when you didn't compare them side by side?
  The index card is longer than the string.
  The sticky note is shorter than the string.
  Which is longer, the index card or the sticky note?

- The marker is shorter than the string. The string is shorter than the crayon. Which is shorter, the marker or the crayon?

- The folder is longer than the string. The book is longer than the string. Which is longer, the folder or the book? (We can't tell.) Explain how you know this.

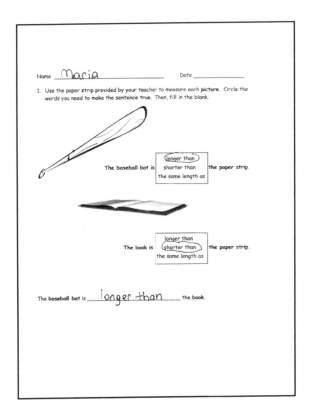

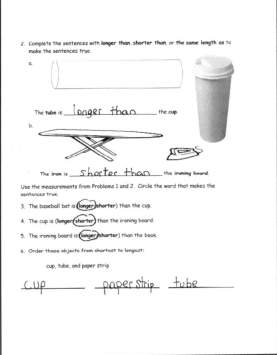

Lesson 2: Compare length using indirect comparison by finding objects *longer than, shorter than,* and *equal in length to* that of a string.

29

© 2015 Great Minds. eureka-math.org
G1-M3-TE-BK3-1.3.1-01.2016

- How was using the paper strip in the Problem Set similar to or different from using the string? How did using the paper strip help you compare the objects in the pictures? Use an example from the Problem Set to explain your thinking.

- Look at the pictures from Page 1. Can we compare the baseball bat and the tube? Why or why not?

- Look at Problem 2(a). How did you set up your paper strip when you measured the cup compared to the tube? Are you still measuring the length of each object? (Yes. It still tells us how long something is. We can measure length in different directions.)

- In the Application Problem today, we were comparing the lengths of three stuffed animals, which can also be considered their **heights**. When we measure length from the ground toward the sky, we usually call that the height. Did any of you compare the length of two objects based on their height? Share your example.

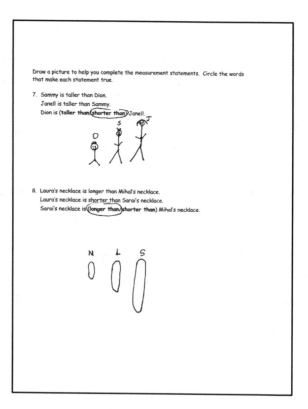

Exit Ticket (3 minutes)

After the Student Debrief, instruct students to complete the Exit Ticket. A review of their work will help with assessing students' understanding of the concepts that were presented in today's lesson and planning more effectively for future lessons. The questions may be read aloud to the students.

Lesson 2:   Compare length using indirect comparison by finding objects *longer than, shorter than,* and *equal in length to* that of a string.

EUREKA MATH

Name _____ Date _____

1. Use the paper strip provided by your teacher to measure each **picture**. Circle the
   words you need to make the sentence true. Then, fill in the blank.

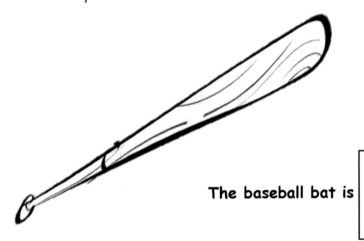

The baseball bat is | longer than
shorter than
the same length as | **the paper strip.**

The book is | longer than
shorter than
the same length as | **the paper strip.**

The **baseball bat** is _____ the **book**.

**EUREKA
MATH**

Lesson 2: Compare length using indirect comparison by finding objects
longer than, shorter than, and *equal in length to* that of a string.

31

© 2015 Great Minds. eureka-math.org
G1-M3-TE-BK3-1.3.1-01.2016

2. Complete the sentences with **longer than**, **shorter than**, or **the same length as** to make the sentences true.

a.

The **tube** is _____ the **cup**.

b.

The **iron** is _____ the **ironing board**.

Use the measurements from Problems 1 and 2. Circle the word that makes the sentences true.

3. The baseball bat is **(longer/shorter)** than the cup.

4. The cup is **(longer/shorter)** than the ironing board.

5. The ironing board is **(longer/shorter)** than the book.

6. Order these objects from shortest to longest:

cup, tube, and paper strip

_____ _____ _____

Lesson 2: Compare length using indirect comparison by finding objects
longer than, shorter than, and *equal in length to* that of a string.

Draw a picture to help you complete the measurement statements. Circle the words that make each statement true.

7. Sammy is taller than Dion.

   Janell is taller than Sammy.

   Dion is (**taller than/shorter than**) Janell.

8. Laura's necklace is longer than Mihal's necklace.

   Laura's necklace is shorter than Sarai's necklace.

   Sarai's necklace is (**longer than/shorter than**) Mihal's necklace.

EUREKA MATH

Lesson 2: Compare length using indirect comparison by finding objects
longer than, shorter than, and *equal in length to* that of a string.

33

© 2015 Great Minds. eureka-math.org
G1-M3-TE-BK3-1.3.1-01.2016

Name _____ Date _____

Draw a picture to help you complete the measurement statements. Circle the words that make each statement true.

Tanya's doll is shorter than Aline's doll.

Mira's doll is taller than Aline's doll.

Tanya's doll is (**taller than/shorter than**) Mira's doll.

Lesson 2: Compare length using indirect comparison by finding objects *longer than, shorter than,* and *equal in length to* that of a string.

© 2015 Great Minds. eureka-math.org
G1-M3-TE-BK3-1.3.1-01.2016

Name _____   Date _____

Use the paper strip provided by your teacher to measure each **picture**. Circle the words you need to make the sentence true. Then, fill in the blank.

1.

The sundae is
| longer than |
| shorter than |
| the same length as |
the paper strip.

The spoon is
| longer than |
| shorter than |
| the same length as |
the paper strip.

The **spoon** is _____ the **sundae**.

2.

The **balloon** is _____ the **cake**.

EUREKA
MATH

Lesson 2:   Compare length using indirect comparison by finding objects
            longer than, shorter than, and *equal in length to* that of a string.

35

3.

The **ball** is shorter than the paper strip.

So, the **shoe** is _____ the **ball**.

Use the measurements from Problems 1-3. Circle the word that makes the sentences true.

4. The spoon is (**longer/shorter**) than the cake.

5. The balloon is (**longer/shorter**) than the sundae.

6. The shoe is (**longer/shorter**) than the balloon.

7. Order these objects from shortest to longest:

cake, spoon, and paper strip

_____   _____   _____

Lesson 2:   Compare length using indirect comparison by finding objects
              longer than, shorter than, and *equal in length to* that of a string.

Draw a picture to help you complete the measurement statements. Circle the word that makes each statement true.

8. Marni's hair is shorter than Wesley's hair.

    Marni's hair is longer than Bita's hair.

    Bita's hair is (**longer/shorter**) than Wesley's hair

9. Elliott is shorter than Brady.

    Sinclair is shorter than Elliott.

    Brady is (**taller/shorter**) than Sinclair.

Lesson 2:   Compare length using indirect comparison by finding objects
              longer than, shorter than, and *equal in length to* that of a string.

37

© 2015 Great Minds. eureka-math.org
G1-M3-TE-BK3-1.3.1-01.2016

0	1	2	3
4	5	<u>6</u>	7
8	<u>9</u>		

Hide Zero cards, numeral side of ones digits (Copy double-sided with the next page.)

Lesson 2:   Compare length using indirect comparison by finding objects
longer than, shorter than, and *equal in length to* that of a string.

EUREKA
MATH

Hide Zero cards, dot side of ones digits (Copy double-sided with the previous page.)

Lesson 2:   Compare length using indirect comparison by finding objects
             longer than, shorter than, and *equal in length to* that of a string.

© 2015 Great Minds. eureka-math.org
G1-M3-TE-BK3-1.3.1-01.2016

39

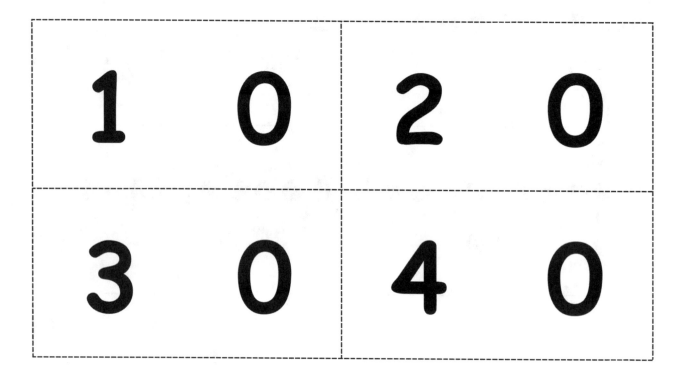

Hide Zero cards, numeral side of tens digits, 10–40 (Copy double-sided with the next page.)

Lesson 2: Compare length using indirect comparison by finding objects
longer than, shorter than, and *equal in length to* that of a string.

EUREKA
MATH

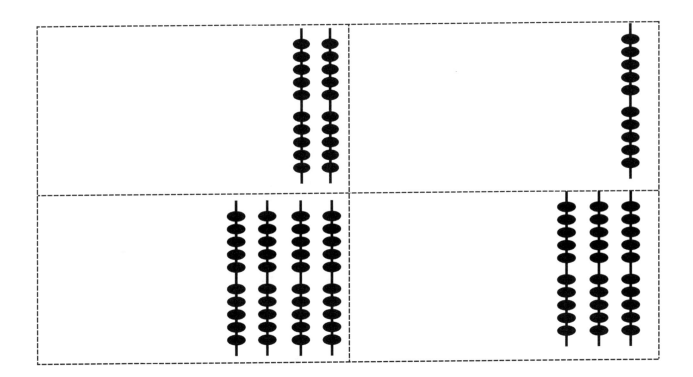

Hide Zero cards, dot side of tens digits, 10–40 (Copy double-sided with the previous page.)

Lesson 2: Compare length using indirect comparison by finding objects
longer than, shorter than, and *equal in length to* that of a string.

41

© 2015 Great Minds. eureka-math.org
G1-M3-TE-BK3-1.3.1-01.2016

0	1	2	3
4	5	6	7
8	9	10	11
12	13	14	15

numeral cards

Lesson 2:   Compare length using indirect comparison by finding objects
longer than, shorter than, and *equal in length to* that of a string.

EUREKA
MATH

If _____ is longer than
(classroom object)
my foot and

_____ is shorter than my
(classroom object)
foot, then

_____ is longer than
(classroom object)

_____.
(classroom object)

My foot is about the same
length as _____.
(classroom object)

_____

indirect comparison statements

Lesson 2:   Compare length using indirect comparison by finding objects
longer than, shorter than, and *equal in length to* that of a string.

43

Lesson 3

Objective: Order three lengths using indirect comparison.

suggested Lesson Structure

- ■ Fluency Practice   (16 minutes)
- ■ Application Problem   (5 minutes)
- ▨ Concept Development   (29 minutes)
- ■ Student Debrief   (10 minutes)

   Total Time   **(60 minutes)**

Fluency Practice (16 minutes)

- Beep Counting **1.NBT.1**   (3 minutes)
- Rekenrek Addition and Subtraction **1.OA.6, 1.NBT.5**   (3 minutes)
- Sprint: Adding and Subtracting Teen Numbers and Ones **1.OA.6**   (10 minutes)

Beep Counting (3 minutes)

Note: This fluency activity strengthens students' ability to understand number relationships and to recognize counting patterns.

Say a series of three or more numbers, but replace one of the numbers with the word *beep* (e.g., 15, 16, beep). When signaled, students say the number that was replaced by the word *beep* in the sequence. Scaffold number sequences, beginning with easy sequences and moving to more complex ones. Be sure to include forward and backward number sequences and to change the sequential placement of the beep.

Continue with the following suggested sequences: 15, 16, beep; 25, 26, beep; 35, 36, beep; 12, 11, beep; 22, 21, beep; 32, 31, beep; 8, beep, 10; 18, beep, 20; 38, beep, 40; beep, 9, 8; beep, 19, 18; and beep, 29, 28. After practicing beep counting by ones, try beep counting by tens, twos, or fives.

Rekenrek Addition and Subtraction (3 minutes)

Materials: (T) 20-bead or 100-bead Rekenrek

Note: This fluency activity reviews the grade level standard of addition and subtraction within 20.

   T: (Show 14 on the Rekenrek.) Say the number.

   S: 14.

   T: Say it the Say Ten way.

   S: Ten 4.

EUREKA
MATH

T: What will my number be if I take out ten?

S: 4.

T: Let's check. (Take out 10.) Yes!

Follow the paradigm to review the following problem types: adding a ten to some ones (e.g., 4 + 10), subtracting a ten from a teen number (e.g., 16 – 10), adding some ones to a teen number (e.g., 13 + 3), and subtracting some ones from a teen number (e.g., 17 – 4).

Sprint: Adding and Subtracting Teen Numbers and Ones (10 minutes)

Materials: (S) Adding and Subtracting Teen Numbers and Ones Sprint

Note: This Sprint addresses the Grade 1 core fluency standard of adding and subtracting within 10 and builds the connection between addition and subtraction within 10 to addition and subtraction with teen numbers.

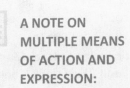

A NOTE ON
MULTIPLE MEANS
OF ACTION AND
EXPRESSION:

When using words unfamiliar to English language learners, be sure to illustrate their meanings by using real objects or by showing pictures while speaking.

Application Problem (5 minutes)

Draw one picture to match both of these sentences:

The book is longer than the index card. The book is shorter than the folder.

Which is longer, the index card or the folder? Write a statement comparing the two objects. Use your drawings to help you answer the question.

Note: This problem applies students' understanding of indirect comparison from Lesson 2. In today's lesson, students continue to work with indirect comparisons, focusing on comparing distances.

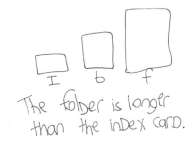

Concept Development (29 minutes)

Materials: (T) Masking tape (two colors, if possible), piece of string or yarn approximately 6–10 feet long (depending on dimensions of the classroom—the string should reach from the door to the middle of the classroom), projector, city blocks grid (Template) (S) Personal white board with city blocks grid (Template)

Note: Prior to math class, choose a spot in the middle of the classroom that diagonally faces the door. From this point, create two paths to the door using different colored masking tape for each path on the floor. One path (the red path) should be shorter (and less circuitous) than the other (the blue path). If the classroom floor has tiles, use their lines to guide the paths. If not, use a string to measure the length of each later in the lesson, or mark the tape with length units in black marker to denote unit lengths without referring to them as such.

Invite students to gather in the meeting area.

T: (Project the city blocks grid.) Mary and Anne are trying to figure out whose path to the park is longer. Here is a map showing Mary's path and Anne's path from each of their houses to the park. How can we figure out which path is longer?

S: Look and see which one seems longer. → Count the boxes from one endpoint to the other. → Measure the paths with a string and compare. → Count each line on the path.

T: Yes! These lines are like city blocks. When you trace from one line to the other line, that's a city block. So, we can count how many city blocks they need to walk in order to get to the park. We don't want to count the squares because we need to trace the path, which is made up *of lines,* not squares.

T: I'm going to trace Mary's path with my marker so I don't lose track. Count the city blocks with me.

S/T: 1, 2, 3, …. (Count until the tracing reaches the park.)

T: How many city blocks long is Mary's path?

S: 11 city blocks long.

T: (Write the number and unit next to Mary's path.)

T: It's your turn to count the city blocks on Anne's path by tracing it with your marker.

S: (Trace each city block, and count as the teacher circulates.)

T: How many city blocks long is Anne's path?

S: 9 city blocks long.

T: Help me count as I trace Anne's path.

T: (Trace and write the number and unit.) Whose path is longer? Mary's or Anne's?

S: Mary's path.

T: If a new girl, Beth, moves into the neighborhood and walks a longer path to get to the park than Mary, whose path is longer, Beth's or Anne's? Turn and talk to your partner about how you know.

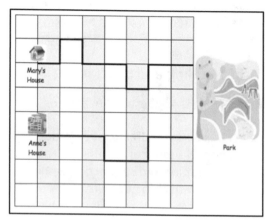

Mary's and Anne's paths on the city blocks grid

A NOTE ON MULTIPLE MEANS OF REPRESENTATION:

If students have trouble tracing and counting the distance of the paths, guide them to write numbers on the lines of the paths as they count.

S: Beth's path will be longer than Anne's because you said Beth's path is longer than Mary's, and we figured out that Mary's path is longer than Anne's. So, Beth's path has to be longer than Anne's.

T: Order the paths from longest to shortest on your personal white board.

S: (Write Beth, Mary, Anne.)

T: Great job comparing the lengths of different paths from the map! Let's try the same thing in our classroom. I'm trying to figure out a path to the door to line up for recess. Should we find the longest path to the door or the shortest path to the door, and why? Talk to your partner.

S: The shortest path because it helps us get to recess sooner!

Lesson 3:   Order three lengths using indirect comparison.

EUREKA MATH

T: Good thinking. So, let's do some comparing with the paths I've created in the classroom. What do you notice about these two paths?

S: The blue one seems longer. It looks like it's making a lot of turns. → The red one seems shorter because I see a lot more of the blue color on the floor.

T: How can we check which is shorter or longer precisely?

S: (Replies vary depending on how the room is set up for this component.) Count the lines just like we counted the city blocks. → We can use a string, just like we did to measure yesterday. → Our floor has squares. We can count those lines.

T: Let's check by counting the tile lines just like we counted the city blocks. (Choose two student volunteers to either step on each line or trace each line as the class counts to figure out the length of each path. Adjust this as necessary according to how the room is set up for the activity.)

T: Which is longer?

S: The blue path.

T: Good job! Do you think there's a shorter way to get to the door than these two paths? Turn and talk to your partner.

S: Yes. Don't make any turns. Just go straight to the door!

T: You are right! (Walk over to and stand where the two paths start. Place a string on the starting point and hold it. Choose a student to take the other end of the string and to walk straight to the door.) Here's the straight line for the shortest path you have suggested. (Cut the string that measures this straight path.)

T: How can we make sure this is the shortest path compared to the other paths?

S: Put the string on the other paths and check.

T: (Have students help hold down the string at every corner as you measure the red path. Stop when the string runs out.)

T: Which path is longer, the straight path or this red path? How can you tell?

S: The red path. It keeps going, but the string ran out. → The shortest path is the straight line!

T: So, if the red path is longer than the string that measures the straight path, which is longer, the straight path or the blue path? Turn and talk to your partner.

S: The blue path is longer because the blue path is longer than the red path, and the red path is longer than the straight path.

T: Excellent job figuring out the shortest path to the door.

Problem Set (10 minutes)

Students should do their personal best to complete the Problem Set within the allotted 10 minutes. For some classes, it may be appropriate to modify the assignment by specifying which problems they work on first. Some problems do not specify a method for solving. Students should solve these problems using the RDW approach used for Application Problems.

Student Debrief (10 minutes)

Lesson Objective: Order three lengths using indirect comparison.

The Student Debrief is intended to invite reflection and active processing of the total lesson experience.

Invite students to review their solutions for the Problem Set. They should check work by comparing answers with a partner before going over answers as a class. Look for misconceptions or misunderstandings that can be addressed in the Debrief. Guide students in a conversation to debrief the Problem Set and process the lesson.

In addition, this is a great place to show the strategy of marking the line segments as they are counted. This strategy could help students with tracking issues.

Any combination of the questions below may be used to lead the discussion.

- Look at the city blocks grid. Think back to the shortest path we made to the door from the middle of the classroom. Draw the shortest path from Anne's house to the park. What does the path look like? Explain why this path is the shortest path.

- What other tools can help measure the shortest distance between the middle of the classroom and the door? How does using a string help measure different paths?

- Can you think of an example where the shortest path that you could take to the door would not be a straight line? (One or more desks might be in the way, etc.)

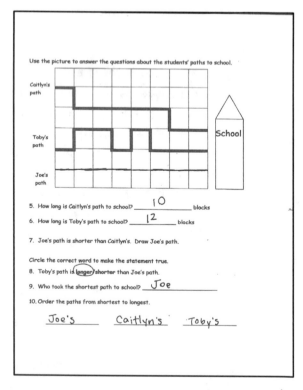

EUREKA MATH

- Explain to your partner how to solve Problem 4.

- Explain to your partner how to solve Problem 6.

- How was solving Problem 3 similar to solving Problem 5?

- Look at today's Application Problem. Order the items from longest to shortest.

Exit Ticket (3 minutes)

After the Student Debrief, instruct students to complete the Exit Ticket. A review of their work will help with assessing students' understanding of the concepts that were presented in today's lesson and planning more effectively for future lessons. The questions may be read aloud to the students.

A

Number Correct: ⬡

Name _____

Date _____

*Write the missing number. Pay attention to the + and − signs.

1.	$5 + 2 = \square$		16.	$13 + 6 = \square$	
2.	$15 + 2 = \square$		17.	$3 + 16 = \square$	
3.	$2 + 5 = \square$		18.	$19 - 2 = \square$	
4.	$12 + 5 = \square$		19.	$19 - 7 = \square$	
5.	$7 - 2 = \square$		20.	$4 + 15 = \square$	
6.	$17 - 2 = \square$		21.	$14 + 5 = \square$	
7.	$7 - 5 = \square$		22.	$18 - 6 = \square$	
8.	$17 - 5 = \square$		23.	$18 - 2 = \square$	
9.	$4 + 3 = \square$		24.	$13 + \square = 19$	
10.	$14 + 3 = \square$		25.	$\square - 6 = 13$	
11.	$3 + 4 = \square$		26.	$14 + \square = 19$	
12.	$13 + 4 = \square$		27.	$\square - 4 = 15$	
13.	$7 - 4 = \square$		28.	$\square - 5 = 14$	
14.	$17 - 4 = \square$		29.	$13 + 4 = 19 - \square$	
15.	$17 - 3 = \square$		30.	$18 - 6 = \square + 3$	

Lesson 3:   Order three lengths using indirect comparison.

EUREKA MATH

B

Number Correct: ☆

Name _____ Date _____

*Write the missing number. Pay attention to the + and - signs.

1.	$5 + 1 = \square$		16.	$12 + 7 = \square$	
2.	$15 + 1 = \square$		17.	$2 + 17 = \square$	
3.	$1 + 5 = \square$		18.	$18 - 2 = \square$	
4.	$11 + 5 = \square$		19.	$18 - 6 = \square$	
5.	$6 - 1 = \square$		20.	$3 + 16 = \square$	
6.	$16 - 1 = \square$		21.	$13 + 6 = \square$	
7.	$6 - 5 = \square$		22.	$17 - 4 = \square$	
8.	$16 - 5 = \square$		23.	$17 - 3 = \square$	
9.	$4 + 5 = \square$		24.	$12 + \square = 18$	
10.	$14 + 5 = \square$		25.	$\square - 6 = 12$	
11.	$5 + 4 = \square$		26.	$13 + \square = 19$	
12.	$15 + 4 = \square$		27.	$\square - 3 = 16$	
13.	$9 - 4 = \square$		28.	$\square - 3 = 17$	
14.	$19 - 4 = \square$		29.	$11 + 6 = 19 - \square$	
15.	$19 - 5 = \square$		30.	$19 - 5 = \square + 3$	

Name _____ Date _____

1. In a playroom, Lu Lu cut a piece of string that measured the distance from the doll house to the park. She took the same string and tried to measure the distance between the park and the store, but she ran out of string!

   Which is the longer path? Circle your answer.

   the doll house to the park

   the park to the store

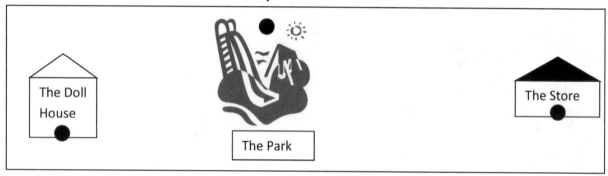

Use the picture to answer the questions about the rectangles.

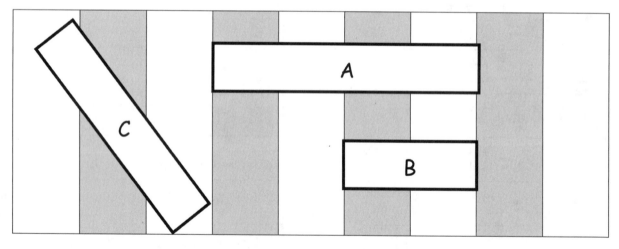

2. Which is the shortest rectangle? _____

3. If Rectangle A is longer than Rectangle C, the longest rectangle is _____.

4. Order the rectangles from shortest to longest:

   _____   _____   _____

Lesson 3:   Order three lengths using indirect comparison.

EUREKA MATH

Use the picture to answer the questions about the students' paths to school.

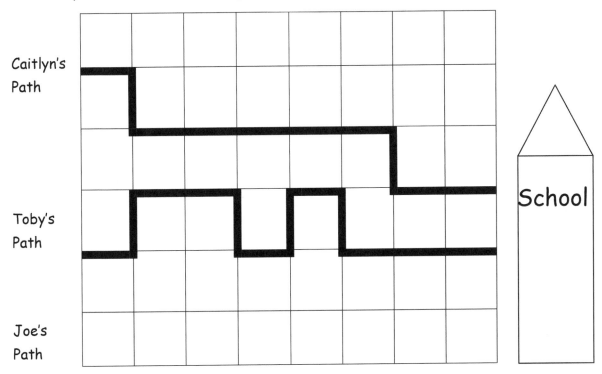

5. How long is Caitlyn's path to school? _____ blocks

6. How long is Toby's path to school? _____ blocks

7. Joe's path is shorter than Caitlyn's. Draw Joe's path.

Circle the correct word to make the statement true.

8. Toby's path is **longer/shorter** than Joe's path.

9. Who took the shortest path to school? _____

10. Order the paths from shortest to longest.

_____   _____   _____

Name _____ Date _____

Use the picture to answer the questions about the students' paths to the museum.

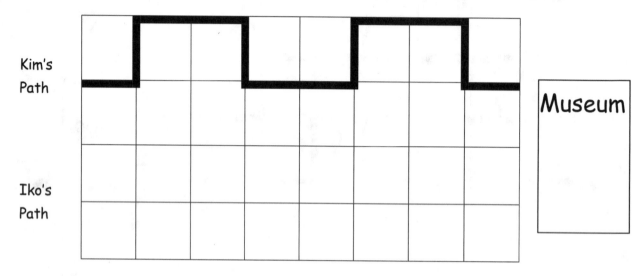

1. How long is Kim's path to the museum? _____ blocks

2. Iko's path is shorter than Kim's path. Draw Iko's path.

Circle the correct word to make the statement true.

3. Kim's path is **longer/shorter** than Iko's path.

4. How long is Iko's path to the museum? _____ blocks

EUREKA MATH

Name _____ Date _____

1. The string that measures the path from the garden to the tree is longer than the path between the tree and the flowers. Circle the shorter path.

the garden to the tree

the tree to the flowers

Garden

Tree

Flowers

Use the picture to answer the questions about the rectangles.

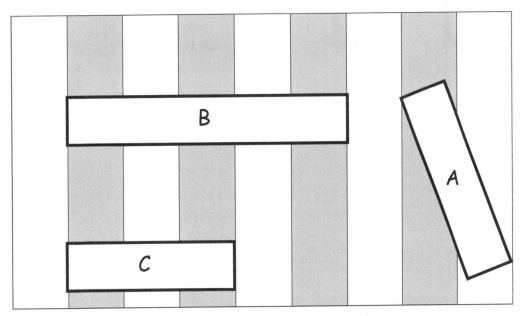

2. Which is the longest rectangle? _____

3. If Rectangle A is longer than Rectangle C, the shortest rectangle is

_____.

4. Order the rectangles from shortest to longest.

_____   _____   _____

Use the picture to answer the questions about the children's paths to the beach.

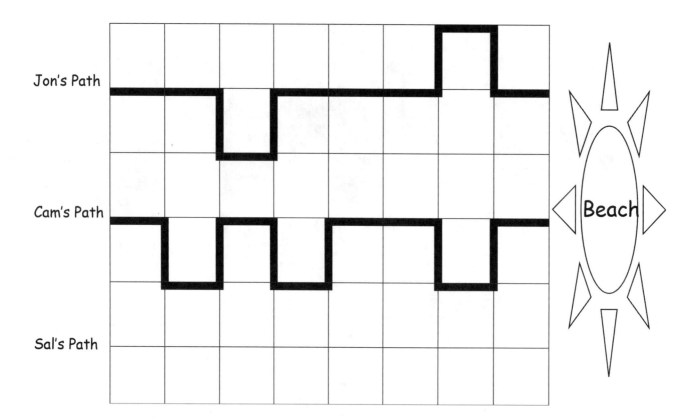

5. How long is Jon's path to the beach? _____ blocks

6. How long is Cam's path to the beach? _____ blocks

7. Jon's path is longer than Sal's path. Draw Sal's path.

Lesson 3:   Order three lengths using indirect comparison.

EUREKA
MATH

Circle the correct word to make the statement true.

8. Cam's path is **longer/shorter** than Sal's path.

9. Who took the shortest path to the beach? _____

10. Order the paths from shortest to longest.

    _____   _____   _____

Mary's
House

Anne's
House

Park

city blocks grid

Lesson 3:   Order three lengths using indirect comparison.

Mathematics Curriculum

Topic B
Standard Length Units

1.MD.1, 1.MD.2

Focus Standards:	1.MD.1	Order three objects by length; compare the lengths of two objects indirectly by using a third object.
	1.MD.2	Express the length of an object as a whole number of length units, by laying multiple copies of a shorter object (the length unit) end to end; understand that the length measurement of an object is the number of same-size length units that span it with no gaps or overlaps. *Limit to contexts where the object being measured is spanned by a whole number of length units with no gaps or overlaps.*
Instructional Days:	3	
Coherence -Links from:	GK–M3	Comparison of Length, Weight, Capacity, and Numbers to 10
-Links to:	G2–M2	Addition and Subtraction of Length Units
	G2–M7	Problem Solving with Length, Money, and Data

Topic B adds a new level of precision to measurement by introducing the idea of a length unit. In Lesson 4, centimeter cubes are laid alongside the length of objects as students learn that the total number of cubes laid end to end with no gaps or overlaps is the length measure of that object. The objects being measured by students include many of the same objects measured in Topic A so that students can add greater precision to their measurements as they specify the number of units equal to the length of the objects being compared. For example, the length of the crayon can now be described not only as shorter than the paper strip, but more precisely as 9 centimeter cubes (**1.MD.2**).

In Lesson 5, students lay those same centimeter cubes alongside a ruler, recognizing the meaning of the numbers on the ruler as describing the number of centimeter length units up to that number. The centimeter then connects students to their world as they come to realize that the centimeter unit is used by first-grade students in Brazil, by the restaurant owner across the street, and even by their families. Students explore the question, "Why would we use a standard unit to measure?" As the use of rulers to measure is a Grade 2 standard, students in Grade 1 simply *rename* their centimeter cube as a centimeter as they continue to use the cubes to measure objects. The Geometric Measurement Progressions Document suggests that students engage in standard unit measurement in order to develop a solid understanding of why and how to measure, rather than measuring using a plethora of nonstandard measurement units.[1]

---

[1]See the K–5 Geometric Measurement progression.

The topic closes with Lesson 6 where students measure and compare sets of three items using centimeter cubes, returning to the transitive statements of Topic A, but with more sophisticated insights (**1.MD.1**): "The pencil measures 10 centimeters. The crayon measures 6 centimeters. The book measures 20 centimeters. The order from shortest to longest is the crayon, the pencil, and the book. The book is longer than the pencil, and the pencil is longer than the crayon, so the book is longer than the crayon." Students finally solve *compare with difference unknown* word problems, determining how much longer a given object is than another.

A Teaching Sequence Toward Mastery of Standard Length Units
Objective 1: Express the length of an object using centimeter cubes as length units to measure with no gaps or overlaps. (Lesson 4)
Objective 2: Rename and measure with centimeter cubes, using their standard unit name of centimeters. (Lesson 5)
Objective 3: Order, measure, and compare the length of objects before and after measuring with centimeter cubes, solving *compare with difference unknown* word problems. (Lesson 6)

Lesson 4

Objective: Express the length of an object using centimeter cubes as length units to measure with no gaps or overlaps.

Suggested Lesson Structure

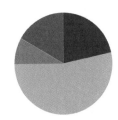

■ Fluency Practice   (13 minutes)
■ Application Problem   (5 minutes)
■ Concept Development   (32 minutes)
■ Student Debrief   (10 minutes)
  Total Time   **(60 minutes)**

Fluency Practice (13 minutes)

- Race and Roll Addition **1.OA.6**   (4 minutes)
- Speed Writing by Twos **1.OA.5**   (3 minutes)
- Subtraction Within 20 **1.OA.6**   (6 minutes)

Race and Roll Addition (4 minutes)

Materials: (S) 1 die per pair

Note: This fluency activity reviews the grade level standard of adding within 20.

Partners start at 0. Partners take turns rolling a die and then saying a number sentence by adding the number rolled to the total. (For example, Partner A rolls 6 and says, "0 + 6 = 6." Partner B rolls 3 and says, "6 + 3 = 9.") They continue rapidly rolling and saying number sentences until they get to 20, without going over. Partners stand when they reach 20. (For example, if partners are at 18 and roll 5, they take turns rolling until one of them rolls 2 or 1 two times. Then, they both stand.)

Speed Writing by Twos (3 minutes)

Materials: (T) Timer (S) Personal white board

Note: This fluency activity provides students practice with writing numbers while reinforcing adding 2.

Time students as they count by twos on their boards from 0 to 40 as fast as they can. Students stand and hold up their boards when they get to 40. To add excitement to the game, give the class a point each time a student gets to 40, and see how many points the class can earn in two minutes.

Record the points to use as a motivator the next time students speed write by twos.

Lesson 4:   Express the length of an object using centimeter cubes as length units
to measure with no gaps or overlaps.

© 2015 Great Minds. eureka-math.org
G1-M3-TE-BK3-1.3.1-01.2016

61

Subtraction Within 20 (6 minutes)

Materials: (T) Hide Zero cards (Lesson 2 Fluency Template 1) enlarged (S) Personal white board

Note: This review fluency activity helps strengthen students' understanding of the take from ten and take from the ones subtraction strategies as well as their ability to recognize appropriate strategies based on problem types.

- T: (Show 14 with Hide Zero cards.) How can I take 14 apart to help me subtract?
- S: 10 and 4.
- T: I want to subtract 2 from 14. Write a number sentence to show whether I should subtract 2 from the 4 or the 10.
- S: (Write 4 – 2 = 2.)
- T: Why wouldn't I take from my 10?
- S: You don't need to because you have enough ones.
- T: Yes! It's much easier to just subtract from my ones! Since 4 – 2 = 2, 14 – 2 is what? Write the subtraction sentence.
- S: (Write 14 – 2 = 12.)
- T: (Replace the 4 Hide Zero card with a 2.) Yes!

Repeat with 14 – 5, eliciting that students need to take from ten because there are not enough ones. Repeat with similar problems.

Application Problem (5 minutes)

Joe ran a string from his room to his sister's room to measure the distance between them. When he tried to use the same string to measure the distance from his room to his brother's room, the string didn't reach! Which room was closer to Joe's room, his sister's or his brother's?

Note: This problem directly applies students' learning from Lesson 3 as students use indirect comparison to compare distances. For many students, such problems can be challenging to visualize on the first read. After reading, encourage students to draw a picture to show each part before answering the question. Reread the problem, pausing long enough for students to draw a picture of the comparison of the string and Joe's sister's room before moving on to read the next sentence. Pictures may vary in many ways. As long as the picture demonstrates that Joe's sister's room is closer than Joe's brother's room, any formation can provide an appropriate representation.

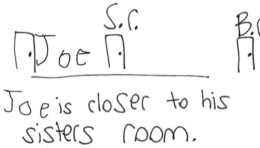

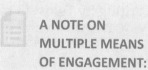

A NOTE ON MULTIPLE MEANS OF ENGAGEMENT:

Challenge students who finish early to try drawing a different way to show their answer or to create their own related problem.

Lesson 4:   Express the length of an object using centimeter cubes as length units to measure with no gaps or overlaps.

EUREKA MATH

Concept Development (32 minutes)

Materials: (T) Projector, new crayon (9 cm), unsharpened pencil (19 cm), small glue stick (8 cm), dry erase marker (12 cm), centimeter cubes (S) Bag with 20 centimeter cubes; bag with a new crayon, unsharpened pencil, small glue stick, dry erase marker, jumbo craft stick (15 cm), and small paper clip (3 cm); measurement recording sheet (Template)

Note: Student bags contain items that are used throughout Topic B, although not all items in the bag are used during today's lesson. Collect the bags at the end of the lesson, and keep them in a safe place for future use. Also, collect the bags with centimeter cubes. The centimeter cubes are sent home for use in completing homework for today's lesson and for Lessons 5 and 6.

Have students sit in the meeting area in a semicircle.

T: (Hold up a new crayon.) How can we find out the length of this crayon? Turn and talk to your partner.

S: Use a string. → Use a ruler.

T: (Project centimeter cubes lined up in a column.) Let's find out how long this crayon is using these **centimeter cubes**. What do you notice about the centimeter cubes?

S: They are all exactly the same size. → They have the same length.

T: Since they have the same length, we can figure out how many centimeter cubes long this crayon is. Count with me as I lay down each centimeter cube to match the length of the crayon. (Lay out the first centimeter cube without aligning it to the crayon's endpoint.)

T/S: 1 centimeter cube.

T: Am I off to a good start?

S: No! You have to line up the endpoints. The edge of the centimeter cube is not starting at the same place as the end of the crayon.

T: You are right! Who can come and start us off on the right foot?

S: (Aligns endpoints.) 1 centimeter cube!

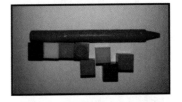

T: Now that our endpoints line up, I can continue to see how many centimeter cubes long this crayon is. (Lay down 3 more centimeter cubes correctly.)

T/S: 2 centimeter cubes! 3 centimeter cubes! 4 centimeter cubes!

T: (Partly overlap the rest of the centimeter cubes by creating an uneven, almost stacked look as pictured to the right.)

T/S: 5 centimeter cubes, 6 centimeter cubes, ..., 11 centimeter cubes!

T: Great. The end of this eleventh centimeter cube lines up with the end of the crayon. So, the crayon is as long as 11 centimeter cubes. Do you agree? Turn and talk to your partner.

S: The centimeter cubes were not laid out correctly. Some parts of the centimeter cubes are under others. Some of them overlap!

MP.3

Lesson 4:   Express the length of an object using centimeter cubes as length units to measure with no gaps or overlaps.

63

© 2015 Great Minds. eureka-math.org
G1-M3-TE-BK3-1.3.1-01.2016

T: You are right. That is not an accurate way to measure this crayon. Let me fix it. (Fix some, but leave a gap between two centimeter cubes.) Okay. So, there are no overlaps. Is this correct?

S: No. There's a space between the centimeter cubes. That's not an accurate way to measure. We can't have any spaces between the centimeter cubes.

T: You are right! The crayon isn't broken with a space in the middle, so the centimeter cubes have to be all connected, without overlaps or gaps. Who would like to come up and fix the centimeter cubes? (Choose a student.)

S: (Lays out 9 centimeter cubes correctly.)

T: Are the centimeter cubes laid out correctly? Are we ready to count and find out how many centimeter cubes long this crayon is?

S: Yes! (Count as teacher points to each centimeter cube.) 1 centimeter cube, 2 centimeter cubes, …, 9 centimeter cubes!

T: How many centimeter cubes long is the crayon?

S: 9 centimeter cubes long!

T: Every centimeter cube is exactly the same length, so we can use them as **length units**. Let's try measuring the pencil with our length units. (Hold up the pencil and the crayon.) What is our length unit called?

S: A centimeter cube.

T: Compared to the crayon, do you think it will take more or fewer of these length units to measure the pencil? Turn and talk to your partner.

S: The pencil will need more centimeter cubes because it is longer than the crayon.

> **A NOTE ON MULTIPLE MEANS OF ENGAGEMENT:**
>
> The abstract term *about* may be difficult for English language learners to understand. While teaching the lesson and using the word *about,* show a visual representation of the objects whenever possible.

Distribute the bags of measuring materials and recording sheets, and have students practice measuring and recording the length of each object from the bag. Students work with their partners as they check each other's work for accuracy. Circulate to provide support for struggling students. If time allows, choose other objects to measure. Long objects can be measured by combining bags of centimeter cubes.

Note: Use the term *about* to describe the length of an object that is not exactly a certain number of centimeter cubes long. For example, if the pencil is closer to 4 centimeter cubes long than to 5, say it is *about* 4 centimeter cubes long.

Lesson 4:   Express the length of an object using centimeter cubes as length units to measure with no gaps or overlaps.

EUREKA MATH

Problem Set (10 minutes)

Students should do their personal best to complete the Problem Set within the allotted 10 minutes. For some classes, it may be appropriate to modify the assignment by specifying which problems they work on first. Some problems do not specify a method for solving. Students should solve these problems using the RDW approach used for Application Problems.

For this Problem Set, all objects are measured horizontally unless otherwise noted by a vertical line next to the object.

Student Debrief (10 minutes)

Lesson Objective: Express the length of an object using centimeter cubes as length units to measure with no gaps or overlaps.

The Student Debrief is intended to invite reflection and active processing of the total lesson experience.

Invite students to review their solutions for the Problem Set. They should check work by comparing answers with a partner before going over answers as a class. Look for misconceptions or misunderstandings that can be addressed in the Debrief. Guide students in a conversation to debrief the Problem Set and process the lesson.

Any combination of the questions below may be used to lead the discussion.

- A **length unit** is what we use to measure how long something is. When we measure, we have to be careful that all of the length units we're using are the same size. What length unit did we measure with today? (**Centimeter cubes.**)

- How is measuring with our new length unit different from measuring with a string, as we did in the last lesson?

- What are the ways in which we need to use the centimeter cubes to accurately measure the length of an object? Explain why these are important.

- Look at Problem 10. What mistake might someone make in answering this question?

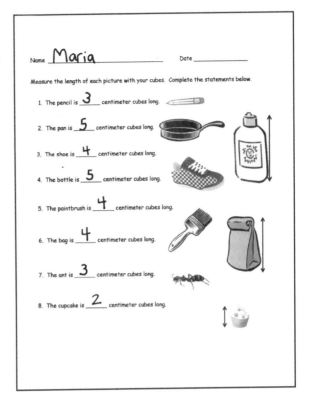

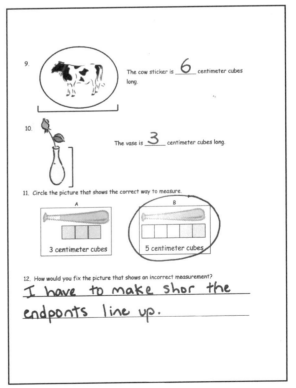

Lesson 4:   Express the length of an object using centimeter cubes as length units to measure with no gaps or overlaps.

65

© 2015 Great Minds. eureka-math.org
G1-M3-TE-BK3-1.3.1-01.2016

- Look at Problem 11. How would you fix the example showing the incorrect way of measuring? Use your own centimeter cubes to correctly measure the length of the smaller bat.

- Can you use the word *tall* to describe the length of an object? Which objects in the Problem Set could be described as being a certain number of centimeter cubes tall?

- Look at your Application Problem. What was Joe using as his tool to compare lengths? Use your hands to show me the length you imagined for his string. Explain your thinking.

Note: Be sure to send the bag of centimeter cubes home for students to complete their homework.

Exit Ticket (3 minutes)

After the Student Debrief, instruct students to complete the Exit Ticket. A review of their work will help with assessing students' understanding of the concepts that were presented in today's lesson and planning more effectively for future lessons. The questions may be read aloud to the students.

Lesson 4: Express the length of an object using centimeter cubes as length units to measure with no gaps or overlaps.

© 2015 Great Minds. eureka-math.org
G1-M3-TE-BK3-1.3.1-01.2016

EUREKA MATH

Name _____   Date _____

Measure the length of each picture with your cubes. Complete the statements below.

1. The pencil is _____ centimeter cubes long.

2. The pan is _____ centimeter cubes long.

3. The shoe is _____ centimeter cubes long.

4. The bottle is _____ centimeter cubes long.

5. The paintbrush is _____ centimeter cubes long.

6. The bag is _____ centimeter cubes long.

7. The ant is _____ centimeter cubes long.

8. The cupcake is _____ centimeter cubes long.

Lesson 4:   Express the length of an object using centimeter cubes as length units to measure with no gaps or overlaps.

© 2015 Great Minds. eureka-math.org
G1-M3-TE-BK3-1.3.1-01.2016

67

9.

The cow sticker is _____ centimeter cubes long.

10.

The vase is _____ centimeter cubes long.

11. Circle the picture that shows the correct way to measure.

A

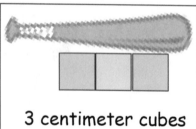

3 centimeter cubes

B

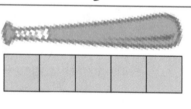

5 centimeter cubes

12. How would you fix the picture that shows an incorrect measurement?

_____

_____

Lesson 4:   Express the length of an object using centimeter cubes as length units to measure with no gaps or overlaps.

EUREKA MATH®

Name _____   Date _____

1.

The picture frame is about _____ centimeter cubes long.

2.

The boy's *crutch* is about _____ centimeter cubes long.

EUREKA
MATH

Lesson 4:   Express the length of an object using centimeter cubes as length units
to measure with no gaps or overlaps.

69

© 2015 Great Minds. eureka-math.org
G1-M3-TE-BK3-1.3.1-01.2016

Name _____   Date _____

Measure the length of each picture with your cubes. Complete the statements below.

1. The lollipop is _____ centimeter cubes long.

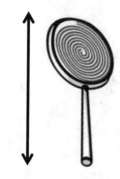

2. The stamp is _____ centimeter cubes long.

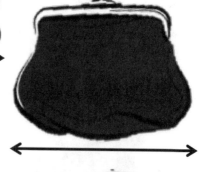

3. The purse is _____ centimeter cubes long.

4. The candle is _____ centimeter cubes long.

Lesson 4:   Express the length of an object using centimeter cubes as length units
to measure with no gaps or overlaps.

EUREKA
MATH

5. The bow is _____ centimeter cubes long.

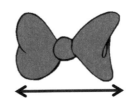

6. The cookie is _____ centimeter cubes long.

7. The mug is about _____ centimeter cubes long.

8. The ketchup is about _____ centimeter cubes long.

9. The envelope is about _____ centimeter cubes long.

EUREKA
MATH.

Lesson 4:   Express the length of an object using centimeter cubes as length units
to measure with no gaps or overlaps.

71

10. Circle the picture that shows the correct way to measure.

A

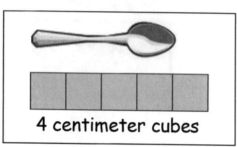

3 centimeter cubes

B

4 centimeter cubes

C

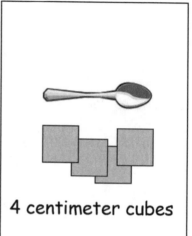

4 centimeter cubes

D

4 centimeter cubes

11. Explain what is wrong with the measurements for the pictures you did NOT circle.

_____

_____

_____

Lesson 4:   Express the length of an object using centimeter cubes as length units to measure with no gaps or overlaps.

EUREKA
MATH

Name _____   Date _____

Classroom Objects	Length Using Centimeter Cubes
glue stick	_____ centimeter cubes long
dry erase marker	_____ centimeter cubes long
craft stick	_____ centimeter cubes long
paper clip	_____ centimeter cubes long
	_____ centimeter cubes long
	_____ centimeter cubes long
	_____ centimeter cubes long

_____

measurement recording sheet

EUREKA
MATH

Lesson 4:   Express the length of an object using centimeter cubes as length units
            to measure with no gaps or overlaps.

© 2015 Great Minds. eureka-math.org
G1-M3-TE-BK3-1.3.1-01.2016

73

Lesson 5

Objective: Rename and measure with centimeter cubes, using their standard unit name of centimeters.

Suggested Lesson Structure

■ Fluency Practice   (17 minutes)
■ Application Problem   (5 minutes)
■ Concept Development   (28 minutes)
■ Student Debrief   (10 minutes)
  Total Time   **(60 minutes)**

Fluency Practice (17 minutes)

▪ Race and Roll Subtraction **1.OA.6**   (4 minutes)
▪ Happy Counting **1.OA.5, 1.NBT.5**   (3 minutes)
▪ Sprint: Subtraction Within 20 **1.OA.6**   (10 minutes)

Race and Roll Subtraction (4 minutes)

Materials: (S) 1 die per pair

Note: This fluency activity reviews the grade level standard of subtracting within 20.

Partners start at 20. Partners take turns rolling the die and saying a number sentence to subtract the number rolled from the total. (For example, Partner A rolls 3 and says, "20 – 3 = 17." Partner B rolls 2 and says, "17 – 2 = 15.") They continue rapidly rolling and saying number sentences until they reach 0. If they roll a number greater than the number they are subtracting from (minuend), they reroll or forfeit their turn. Partners stand when they reach 0. (For example, if partners are at 1 and roll 4, they would take turns rolling until one of them rolls a 1. They would then say, "1 – 1 = 0," and both partners would stand.) Repeat the game as time permits.

Happy Counting (3 minutes)

Note: Practice with counting forward and backward by tens and ones strengthens students' understanding of place value. Counting by twos and fives builds students' ability to count on or back and strengthens addition and subtraction skills.

Repeat the Happy Counting activity from Lesson 2. Choose a counting pattern and range based on the skill level of the class. If students are proficient with counting by ones, twos, fives, and tens up to 40, start at 40, and quickly go up to 80. If they are proficient between 40 and 80, Happy Count between 80 and 120. To reinforce place value understanding, alternate between counting the regular way and the Say Ten way.

Lesson 5:   Rename and measure with centimeter cubes, using their standard
              unit name of centimeters.

Sprint: Subtraction Within 20 (10 minutes)

Materials: (S) Subtraction Within 20 Sprint

Note: This Sprint addresses the Grade 1 standard of subtracting within 20.

Application Problem (5 minutes)

Amy used centimeter cubes to measure the length of her book. She used 8 yellow centimeter cubes and 4 red centimeter cubes. How many centimeter cubes long was her book?

Remind students to use the RDW process. After reading (or listening to) the problem, they must be sure to draw, write a number sentence, and write a statement that answers the question.

Note: This problem uses the context of measurement while enabling students to review their processes for adding single digits with a sum of a teen number. Take note of the strategies students are using independently. Are they making ten first? Are they counting on? Are they counting all after drawing the picture? During the Student Debrief, students have the opportunity to connect, or rename, the length unit of centimeter cube to the more common length unit of centimeter.

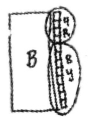

Concept Development (28 minutes)

Materials: (T) Projector, centimeter cubes, string, scissors, centimeter ruler (S) Per pair: bag with at least 12 centimeter cubes (used in Lesson 4), centimeter ruler, pair of dice

Have students sit in the meeting area in a semicircle.

- T: I need your help solving a problem. My mom is traveling to different countries. She wants to get me bracelets from Korea, Brazil, and France. The problem is she wants to make sure they fit, but the bracelets are over there and my wrist is here! What can she do? Is there any way we can help her? Talk to your partner.

- S: We could measure your wrist with centimeter cubes! → That seems hard though; her wrist isn't straight. → We could measure your wrist with a string then!

- T: I love all of your ideas about the different tools we can use. I knew I could rely on you for some great problem solving! Which will be easier to use first, the string or the centimeter cubes?

- S: The string because it can wrap around your wrist.

- T: (Wrap a string around your wrist.) I'll pretend that the string is the bracelet. I'm going to leave a little room so it's not so tight. (Cut.)

- T: (Project the string on the board.) How can we figure out how long this string is? Turn and talk to your partner about how we can measure accurately.

- S: Use centimeter cubes. → Line up the endpoints. → Don't leave any gaps between the cubes. → Don't overlap the cubes.

Lesson 5:   Rename and measure with centimeter cubes, using their standard unit name of centimeters.

75

T: These are important rules for measuring accurately. Let's count and see how many centimeter cubes long the string is as I lay down each cube.

S: 1 cube, 2 cubes, …, 18 cubes!

T: (Project a centimeter ruler.) Here's a tool that my mom is able to use to measure the length of the bracelet. She said every store, no matter what country she's in, uses the centimeter ruler to measure their bracelets. In fact, no matter where you live in the world, people use these tools to measure the length of any items. This tool is called a…?

S: Ruler!

T: When have you seen a ruler used before? Turn and talk to your partner.

S: We used it to draw straight lines in kindergarten. → I used it to learn my counting numbers with my aunt. → My grandpa uses it to measure the picture frames he makes.

T: (Project the centimeter ruler.) What do you notice on the ruler?

S: There are numbers going in order. → There are longer lines next to each number. There are some shorter lines, too.

T: Let's see how the ruler compares to our centimeter cubes that we used to measure my wrist. I'm going to lay these 18 centimeter cubes alongside the ruler. I need to line up the first cube with the endpoint of the ruler. Here's 1 centimeter cube. (Lay down 1 cube.) What do you notice?

S: The other end of the centimeter cube lines up with the 1 on the ruler!

T: When something reaches this line (point to 1 cm mark on the ruler), we say that it is 1 **centimeter** long. So, how long is this centimeter cube?

S: 1 centimeter!

T: (Lay down the second cube.) What do you notice now?

S: The end of the second centimeter cube lines up with the 2 on the ruler!

T: How many centimeters long are these 2 cubes together?

S: 2 centimeters!

T: (Repeat for the third and fourth cubes.) If I lay down the next centimeter cube, with what number will it line up?

S: 5. That's 5 centimeters.

T: (Continue with all the cubes, eliciting responses and checking them by laying down cubes.) How many centimeters long are all of these centimeter cubes?

S: 18 centimeters!

T: When we are measuring with centimeter cubes, we are using the same length unit as the people who use rulers! With this ruler, we are measuring in centimeters. That's the length unit, so we have a special name for this ruler. We call it the **centimeter ruler**. So, did we solve the problem? What should I tell my mom about buying the right length bracelet?

S: Yes! Tell her to buy bracelets that are 18 centimeters long! She can use the ruler to measure 18 centimeters.

> **A NOTE ON MULTIPLE MEANS OF REPRESENTATION:**
>
> Students may continue to use centimeter cubes if they do not demonstrate an understanding of the relationship between a centimeter and centimeter cubes.

Lesson 5:   Rename and measure with centimeter cubes, using their standard unit name of centimeters.

EUREKA MATH®

T: Thank you for helping me solve this problem! I will write to her and let her know! From now on, when we measure, we can say that the length of the item is " _____ centimeters" instead of saying " _____ centimeter cubes." Now, it's your turn to determine for sure that 1 centimeter cube is 1 centimeter long, 3 centimeter cubes are 3 centimeters long, and 6 centimeter cubes are…?

S: 6 centimeters long.

Distribute a bag to each pair of students. Have students practice laying down their centimeter cubes alongside the centimeter ruler and renaming *centimeter cubes* as *centimeters* by following these steps:

1. Roll the dice (e.g., 2 and 5).

2. Partner 1 lays down the centimeter cubes alongside the ruler to show the number from the first die (gets to 2 centimeters on the ruler by laying down 2 centimeter cubes). He says, "I measured to 2 centimeters."

3. Partner 2 adds more centimeter cubes alongside the ruler based on the second die (gets to 7 centimeters on the ruler by laying down 5 centimeter cubes). She says, "Now, we measured to 7 centimeters."

4. Say the addition sentence that tells the length of your cubes. (2 centimeters + 5 centimeters = 7 centimeters.)

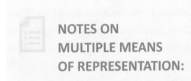

NOTES ON MULTIPLE MEANS OF REPRESENTATION:

Students with disabilities may need some assistance lining up and measuring with centimeter cubes. Model how to use them one on one, and then help with a few measurements.

Note: If time permits, provide an opportunity for students to work with their partners to measure their own bracelet size or watch size. Students loop string around their wrists, cut it, and use centimeter cubes to determine the length. An ELA connection could include having students write home to their families about the size of their wrists, just as the teacher communicated with her family.

Problem Set (10 minutes)

Students should do their personal best to complete the Problem Set within the allotted 10 minutes. For some classes, it may be appropriate to modify the assignment by specifying which problems they work on first. Some problems do not specify a method for solving. Students should solve these problems using the RDW approach used for Application Problems.

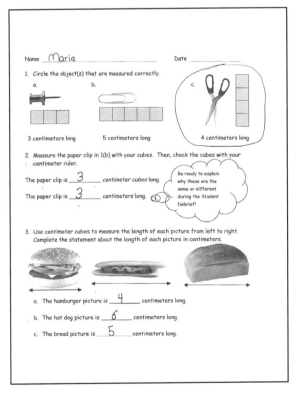

Lesson 5: Rename and measure with centimeter cubes, using their standard unit name of centimeters.

77

© 2015 Great Minds. eureka-math.org
G1-M3-TE-BK3-1.3.1-01.2016

Student Debrief (10 minutes)

Lesson Objective: Rename and measure with centimeter cubes, using their standard unit name of centimeters.

The Student Debrief is intended to invite reflection and active processing of the total lesson experience.

Invite students to review their solutions for the Problem Set. They should check work by comparing answers with a partner before going over answers as a class. Look for misconceptions or misunderstandings that can be addressed in the Debrief. Guide students in a conversation to debrief the Problem Set and process the lesson.

Any combination of the questions below may be used to lead the discussion.

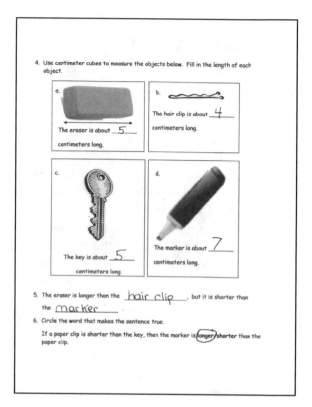

- What is the new length unit we used to measure length accurately? (**Centimeters.**)

- How can you prove to another first grader that 1 centimeter cube is the same as 1 centimeter?

- How are centimeter cubes similar to and different from the centimeters on a **centimeter ruler**?

- Do you think centimeter rulers in Asia or Europe, or anywhere else, look the same as centimeter rulers here? Explain your thinking.

- Why do you think people all over the world use centimeters as a length unit? Why is it important that we all use the same length unit, like centimeters?

- Look at Problem 2. Explain why your measurements are the same or different.

- How did you solve today's Application Problem? Tell your partner your answer using the new length unit as if we used a ruler to measure the length of Amy's book.

Note: Send the bags of centimeter cubes home with students for use in completing their homework.

Exit Ticket (3 minutes)

After the Student Debrief, instruct students to complete the Exit Ticket. A review of their work will help with assessing students' understanding of the concepts that were presented in today's lesson and planning more effectively for future lessons. The questions may be read aloud to the students.

A

Number Correct: _____

Name _____ Date _____

*Write the missing number.

1.	17 - 1 = □		16.	19 - 9 = □	
2.	15 - 1 = □		17.	18 - 9 = □	
3.	19 - 1 = □		18.	11 - 9 = □	
4.	15 - 2 = □		19.	16 - 5 = □	
5.	17 - 2 = □		20.	15 - 5 = □	
6.	18 - 2 = □		21.	14 - 5 = □	
7.	18 - 3 = □		22.	12 - 5 = □	
8.	18 - 5 = □		23.	12 - 6 = □	
9.	17 - 5 = □		24.	14 - □ = 11	
10.	19 - 5 = □		25.	14 - □ = 10	
11.	17 - 7 = □		26.	14 - □ = 9	
12.	18 - 7 = □		27.	15 - □ = 9	
13.	19 - 7 = □		28.	□ - 7 = 9	
14.	19 - 2 = □		29.	19 - 5 = 16 - □	
15.	19 - 7 = □		30.	15 - 8 = □ - 9	

B

Number Correct:

Name _____   Date _____

*Write the missing number.

1.	16 - 1 = ☐		16.	19 - 9 = ☐	
2.	14 - 1 = ☐		17.	18 - 9 = ☐	
3.	18 - 1 = ☐		18.	12 - 9 = ☐	
4.	19 - 2 = ☐		19.	19 - 8 = ☐	
5.	17 - 2 = ☐		20.	18 - 8 = ☐	
6.	15 - 2 = ☐		21.	17 - 8 = ☐	
7.	15 - 3 = ☐		22.	14 - 5 = ☐	
8.	17 - 5 = ☐		23.	13 - 5 = ☐	
9.	19 - 5 = ☐		24.	12 - ☐ = 7	
10.	16 - 5 = ☐		25.	16 - ☐ = 10	
11.	16 - 6 = ☐		26.	16 - ☐ = 9	
12.	19 - 6 = ☐		27.	17 - ☐ = 9	
13.	17 - 6 = ☐		28.	☐ - 7 = 9	
14.	17 - 1 = ☐		29.	19 - 4 = 17- ☐	
15.	17 - 6 = ☐		30.	16 - 8 = ☐ - 9	

Lesson 5:   Rename and measure with centimeter cubes, using their standard
unit name of centimeters.

EUREKA MATH

Name _____ Date _____

1. Circle the object(s) that are measured correctly.

a.

3 centimeters long

b.

5 centimeters long

c.

4 centimeters long

2. Measure the paper clip in 1(b) with your cubes. Then, check the cubes with your centimeter ruler.

The paper clip is _____ *centimeter cubes* long.

The paper clip is _____ *centimeters* long.

> Be ready to explain why these are the same or different during the Debrief!

3. Use centimeter cubes to measure the length of each picture from left to right. Complete the statement about the length of each picture in centimeters.

a. The hamburger picture is _____ centimeters long.

b. The hot dog picture is _____ centimeters long.

c. The bread picture is _____ centimeters long.

 EUREKA MATH®

Lesson 5:   Rename and measure with centimeter cubes, using their standard unit name of centimeters.

81

© 2015 Great Minds. eureka-math.org
G1-M3-TE-BK3-1.3.1-01.2016

4. Use centimeter cubes to measure the objects below. Fill in the length of each object.

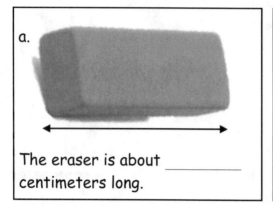

a.

The eraser is about _____ centimeters long.

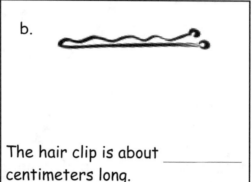

b.

The hair clip is about _____ centimeters long.

c.

The key is about _____ centimeters long.

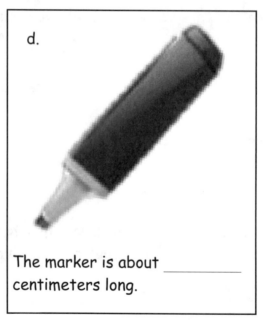

d.

The marker is about _____ centimeters long.

5. The eraser is longer than the _____, but it is shorter than the _____.

6. Circle the word that makes the sentence true.

If a paper clip is shorter than the key, then the marker is **longer/shorter** than the paper clip.

Lesson 5: Rename and measure with centimeter cubes, using their standard unit name of centimeters.

EUREKA MATH

Name _____   Date _____

Use the centimeter cubes to measure the items. Complete the sentences.

1. The water bottle is about _____ centimeters tall.

2. The melon is about _____ centimeters long.

3. The screw is about _____ centimeters long.

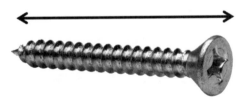

4. The umbrella is about _____ centimeters tall.

EUREKA MATH®

Lesson 5:   Rename and measure with centimeter cubes, using their standard unit name of centimeters.

83

Name _____ Date _____

1. Justin collects stickers. Use centimeter cubes to measure Justin's stickers. Complete the sentences about Justin's stickers.

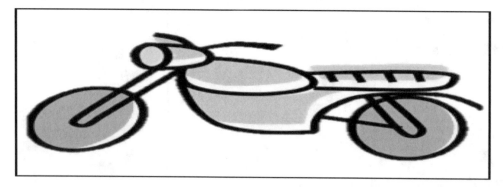

a. The motorcycle sticker is _____ centimeters long.

b. The car sticker is _____ centimeters long.

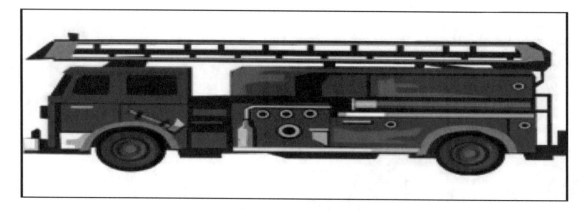

c. The fire truck sticker is _____ centimeters long.

Lesson 5: Rename and measure with centimeter cubes, using their standard unit name of centimeters.

EUREKA
MATH

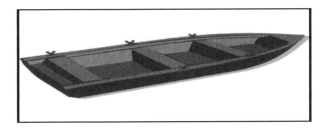

d. The rowboat sticker is _____ centimeters long.

e. The airplane sticker is _____ centimeters long.

2. Use the stickers' measurements to order the stickers of the **fire truck**, the **rowboat**, and the **airplane** from longest to shortest. You can use drawings or names to order the stickers.

Longest ⟶ Shortest

EUREKA MATH

Lesson 5: Rename and measure with centimeter cubes, using their standard unit name of centimeters.

85

© 2015 Great Minds. eureka-math.org
G1-M3-TE-BK3-1.3.1-01.2016

3. Fill in the blanks to make the statements true. (There may be more than one correct answer.)

   a. The airplane sticker is longer than the _____ sticker.

   b. The rowboat sticker is longer than the _____ sticker and shorter

   than the _____ sticker.

   c. The motorcycle sticker is shorter than the _____ sticker and longer

   than the _____ sticker.

   d. If Justin gets a new sticker that is longer than the rowboat, it will also be longer

   than which of his other stickers? _____

Lesson 5:   Rename and measure with centimeter cubes, using their standard
unit name of centimeters.

© 2015 Great Minds. eureka-math.org
G1-M3-TE-BK3-1.3.1-01.2016

Lesson 6

Objective: Order, measure, and compare the length of objects before and after measuring with centimeter cubes, solving *compare with difference unknown* word problems.

Suggested Lesson Structure

■ Fluency Practice   (13 minutes)
■ Application Problem   (5 minutes)
■ Concept Development   (32 minutes)
■ Student Debrief   (10 minutes)
   Total Time   **(60 minutes)**

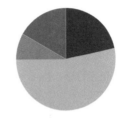

Fluency Practice (13 minutes)

- Addition with Cards **1.OA.6**   (7 minutes)
- Speed Writing by Twos **1.OA.5**   (3 minutes)
- Cold Call: Number Sentence Swap **1.OA.4** (3 minutes)

Addition with Cards (7 minutes)

Materials: (S) Numeral cards 0–10 (Lesson 2 Fluency Template 2), counters (if needed)

Note: This review fluency activity strengthens students' abilities to add within and across ten.

Students sit in partnerships. Students shuffle or mix their numeral cards. Each partner places her deck of cards face down. Each partner flips over two cards and adds her cards together. The partner with the greater total keeps the cards played by both players that round. For example Player A draws 4 and 5 and gives the total 9. Player B draws 9 and 4 and gives the total, 13. Since 9<13, Player B keeps the cards. If the sums are equal, the cards are set aside, and the winner of the next round keeps the cards from both rounds. At the end of the game, the players will each be left with 1 card. They each flip their last card over and the player with the highest card says the sum and collects the cards. Students continue to play as time allows.

Lesson 6:   Order, measure, and compare the length of objects before and after measuring with centimeter cubes, solving *compare with difference unknown* word problems.

87

© 2015 Great Minds. eureka-math.org
G1-M3-TE-BK3-1.3.1-01.2016

Speed Writing by Twos (3 minutes)

Materials: (T) Timer (S) Personal white board

Note: This fluency activity provides students practice with writing numbers while reinforcing adding 2.

Time students as they count by twos on their personal white boards from 0 to 40 as fast as they can. Students stand and hold up their boards when they get to 40. To add excitement to the game, give the class a point each time a student gets to 40, and see how many points the class can earn in two minutes. Record the points, and compare the score with the last time students completed the Speed Writing by Twos fluency activity. Keep a record of points scored each time this fluency activity is done to help students recognize and celebrate improvement.

Cold Call: Number Sentence Swap (3 minutes)

Note: This fluency activity reviews the grade level standard of understanding subtraction as an unknown addend problem and prepares students for *compare with difference unknown* problem types in this lesson.

In Cold Call, the teacher asks a question, pauses to provide think time, and then randomly calls on a student or group of students to answer. This game helps motivate all students to mentally solve the problem so they are ready if they are chosen to answer.

> T: 4 + what number = 5? (Pause.) Kira?
>
> S: (Only Kira answers.) 1.
>
> T: Good. So, 14 + what number = 15? (Pause to provide think time.) Marcus?
>
> S: (Only Marcus answers.) 1.

Continue with the following suggested sequence: 5 + ☐ = 7, 15 + ☐ = 17, 4 + ☐ = 8, and 14 + ☐ = 18.

NOTES ON MULTIPLE MEANS OF ACTION AND EXPRESSION:

When playing games where students are randomly called on to answer, adjust wait time for certain students. Some students may also benefit from hearing the question ahead of time so that they feel prepared when put on the spot in front of their peers.

Application Problem (5 minutes)

Julia's lollipop is 15 centimeters long. She measured the lollipop with 9 red centimeter cubes and some blue centimeter cubes. How many blue centimeter cubes did she use? Remember to use the RDW process.

Note: This problem enables students to continue working with *take apart with difference unknown* problem types within the context of measurement. During the Student Debrief, students compare the length of Julia's lollipop with another item from the lesson to determine how much longer the lollipop is compared to the other item.

$$9 + \boxed{6} = 15$$

She used 6 blue cubes.

Lesson 6:   Order, measure, and compare the length of objects before and after measuring with centimeter cubes, solving *compare with difference unknown* word problems.

Concept Development (32 minutes)

Materials: (T) Projector, unsharpened pencil (19 cm), new crayon (9 cm), small paper clip (3 cm), dry erase marker (12 cm), jumbo craft stick (15 cm), new colored pencil (17 cm), centimeter cubes
(S) Bag with centimeter cubes, bag with various classroom objects (Lesson 4), personal white board

Gather students in the meeting area.

T: (Project dry erase marker, crayon, and new colored pencil in a disorganized way.) Without measuring, can you order these three objects from shortest to longest?

S: It's hard to tell which is longer or shorter. → They seem too similar. We couldn't tell for sure. → Let's straighten them out and line up the endpoints. → We should use our centimeter cubes to be sure.

T: (Align the endpoints of each object.) Now can you order the objects from shortest to longest? Share your thoughts with your partner.

S: (Discuss.) The objects from shortest to longest are the crayon, the dry erase marker, and the colored pencil.

T: (Order the objects as stated by students.) Yes. That's correct!

T: What can we do to describe their lengths more precisely? How can we tell how long each item is?

S: We can measure them!

T: Take the dry erase marker, crayon, and colored pencil out of your bag, and let's measure each item using centimeter cubes. On your personal white board, write down the length of each item.

S: (Measure the items and record their lengths.)

T: What is the length of each item?

S: (Share the measurements. Record the length next to each object.)

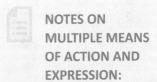

NOTES ON MULTIPLE MEANS OF ACTION AND EXPRESSION:

When students turn and talk with a partner, they are hearing different ways their peers are thinking about measurement. Hearing others talk about measurement more than once helps English language learners understand and acquire language around this topic.

T: (Touch each object while describing its length.) The colored pencil, which is 17 centimeters, is longer than the dry erase marker, which is 12 centimeters. The dry erase marker is longer than the crayon, which is only 9 centimeters. What can you say about the colored pencil compared to the crayon?

S: The colored pencil is longer than the crayon!

T: Look at the measurements next to each object in order from shortest to longest. What do you notice? Talk with your partner. (Circulate and listen.)

S: (Discuss.) The numbers get larger. → The measurements are larger.

Lesson 6: Order, measure, and compare the length of objects before and after measuring with centimeter cubes, solving *compare with difference unknown* word problems.

89

T: Let's compare the number of cubes we used to measure the marker with the number of cubes we used to measure the crayon. (Align the two objects' endpoints. Use centimeter cubes to show their length, as shown on the next page.) Remind me, which object is longer?

S: The marker.

T: How many centimeter cubes did you use to measure the marker?

S: 12 cubes.

T: How many centimeter cubes did you use to measure the crayon?

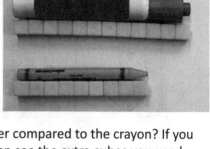

S: 9 cubes.

T: How many more cubes did you need to use to measure the marker compared to the crayon? If you need to, put your rows of cubes right next to each other so you can see the extra cubes you used more easily.

S: (Adjust rows of cubes as necessary to compare.) Three more centimeter cubes.

T: How did you know? Talk with your partner about your thinking. Think about the number sentence that would match what you did.

S: I lined them up and counted on the extras. Niiiine, 10, 11, 12. That's 3 more cubes. → I thought, "9 plus the mystery number gives me 12." Then from 9, I counted on to get to 12. → I took away 9 from 12 and got 3.

T: (Elicit and write a number sentence corresponding to each student response.) You are right! Let's try some more.

Repeat the process with a new pencil, a paper clip, and a craft stick. After comparing the length of two rows of cubes for two of the objects and identifying the difference, encourage students to write the number sentences and the statement on their personal white boards.

Note: Comparing centimeter cubes is a natural opportunity to concretely experience the *compare with difference unknown* problem type. Lesson 9 is dedicated to focusing attention on this objective. Make note of the particular challenges students may be facing, and use these specific examples to help shape the Concept Development work during Lesson 9.

Problem Set (10 minutes)

Students should do their personal best to complete the Problem Set within the allotted 10 minutes. For some classes, it may be appropriate to modify the assignment by specifying which problems they work on first. Some problems do not specify a method for solving. Students should solve these problems using the RDW approach used for Application Problems.

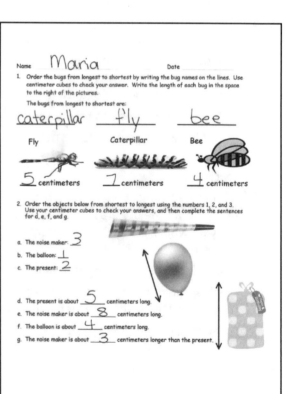

Lesson 6:   Order, measure, and compare the length of objects before and after measuring with centimeter cubes, solving *compare with difference unknown* word problems.

© 2015 Great Minds. eureka-math.org
G1-M3-TE-BK3-1.3.1-01.2016

EUREKA
MATH

Student Debrief (10 minutes)

Lesson Objective: Order, measure, and compare the length of objects before and after measuring with centimeter cubes, solving *compare with difference unknown* word problems.

The Student Debrief is intended to invite reflection and active processing of the total lesson experience.

Invite students to review their solutions for the Problem Set. They should check work by comparing answers with a partner before going over answers as a class. Look for misconceptions or misunderstandings that can be addressed in the Debrief. Guide students in a conversation to debrief the Problem Set and process the lesson.

Any combination of the questions below may be used to lead the discussion.

- What did we do to figure out precisely how much longer or shorter one object was than another today?

- Can you think of a time when it would be helpful or important to say that something is longer by an exact amount rather than just saying it is longer or shorter?

- Turn and talk to your partner about how you solved Problem 3. How are your strategies similar and/or different?

- How was solving Problem 5 different from solving Problems 3 and 4? Explain your thinking.

- Look at your Application Problem. How much longer is Julia's lollipop than the new crayon? Talk with a partner to discuss how you know.

Note: Be sure to send the bag of cubes home for students to complete their homework.

> Use your centimeter cubes to model each length and answer the question. Write a statement for your answer.
>
> 3. Peter's toy T. rex is 11 centimeters tall, and his toy Velociraptor is 6 centimeters tall. How much taller is the T. rex than the Velociraptor?
>
> T- Rex is 5 centimeters taller.
>
> 4. Miguel's pencil rolled 17 centimeters, and Sonya's pencil rolled 9 centimeters. How much less did Sonya's pencil roll than Miguel's?
>
> Sonya's pencil rolled 8 centimeters less.
>
> 5. Tania makes a cube tower that is 3 centimeters taller than Vince's tower. If Vince's tower is 9 centimeters tall, how tall is Tania's tower?
>
> Tania's tower is 12 centimeters

Exit Ticket (3 minutes)

After the Student Debrief, instruct students to complete the Exit Ticket. A review of their work will help with assessing students' understanding of the concepts that were presented in today's lesson and planning more effectively for future lessons. The questions may be read aloud to the students.

Lesson 6: Order, measure, and compare the length of objects before and after measuring with centimeter cubes, solving *compare with difference unknown* word problems.

© 2015 Great Minds. eureka-math.org
G1-M3-TE-BK3-1.3.1-01.2016

91

Name _____ Date _____

1. Order the bugs from longest to shortest by writing the bug names on the lines. Use centimeter cubes to check your answer. Write the length of each bug in the space to the right of the pictures.

   The bugs from longest to shortest are

   _____ _____ _____

   ### Fly

   ____ centimeters

   ### Caterpillar

   ____ centimeters

   ### Bee

   ____ centimeters

Lesson 6:   Order, measure, and compare the length of objects before and after measuring with centimeter cubes, solving *compare with difference unknown* word problems.

EUREKA MATH

© 2015 Great Minds. eureka-math.org
G1-M3-TE-BK3-1.3.1-01.2016

2. Order the objects below from shortest to longest using the numbers 1, 2, and 3. Use your centimeter cubes to check your answers, and then complete the sentences for problems d, e, f, and g.

a. The noise maker: _____

b. The balloon: _____

c. The present: _____

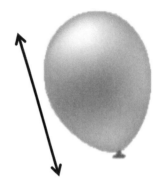

d. The present is about _____ centimeters long.

e. The noise maker is about _____ centimeters long.

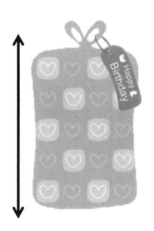

f. The balloon is about _____ centimeters long.

g. The noise maker is about _____ centimeters longer than the present.

EUREKA MATH

Lesson 6: Order, measure, and compare the length of objects before and after measuring with centimeter cubes, solving *compare with difference unknown* word problems.

93

© 2015 Great Minds. eureka-math.org
G1-M3-TE-BK3-1.3.1-01.2016

Use your centimeter cubes to model each length, and answer the question. Write a statement for your answer.

3. Peter's toy T. rex is 11 centimeters tall, and his toy Velociraptor is 6 centimeters tall. How much taller is the T. rex than the Velociraptor?

4. Miguel's pencil rolled 17 centimeters, and Sonya's pencil rolled 9 centimeters. How much less did Sonya's pencil roll than Miguel's?

5. Tania makes a cube tower that is 3 centimeters taller than Vince's tower. If Vince's tower is 9 centimeters tall, how tall is Tania's tower?

Lesson 6: Order, measure, and compare the length of objects before and after measuring with centimeter cubes, solving *compare with difference unknown* word problems.

EUREKA
MATH

Name _____   Date _____

Read the measurements of the tool pictures.

The wrench is 8 centimeters long.

The screwdriver is 12 centimeters long.

The hammer is 9 centimeters long.

1. Order the pictures of the tools from shortest to longest.

_____   _____   _____

2. How much longer is the screwdriver than the wrench?

The screwdriver is _____ centimeters longer than the wrench.

 EUREKA MATH

Lesson 6:   Order, measure, and compare the length of objects before and after measuring with centimeter cubes, solving *compare with difference unknown* word problems.

95

© 2015 Great Minds. eureka-math.org
G1-M3-TE-BK3-1.3.1-01.2016

Name _____   Date _____

1. Natasha's teacher wants her to put the fish in order from longest to shortest. Measure each fish with the centimeter cubes that your teacher gave you.

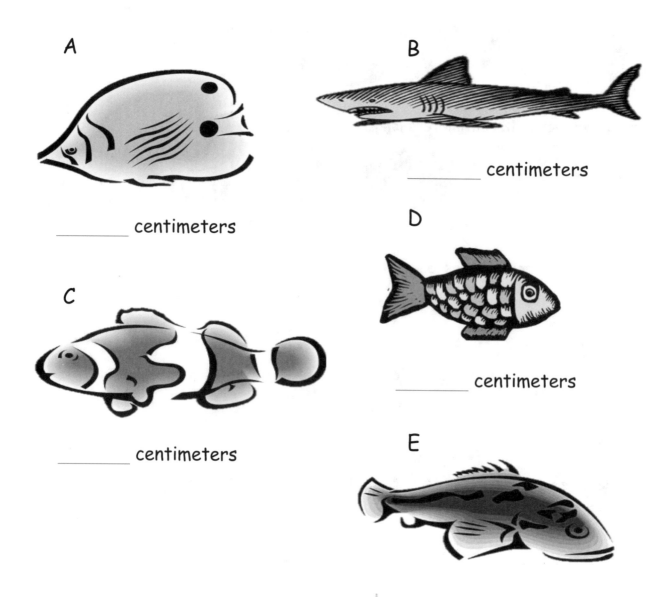

A

_____ centimeters

B

_____ centimeters

C

_____ centimeters

D

_____ centimeters

E

2. Order fish A, B, and C from longest to shortest. _____ centimeters

_____   _____   _____

Lesson 6:   Order, measure, and compare the length of objects before and after measuring with centimeter cubes, solving *compare with difference unknown* word problems.

© 2015 Great Minds. eureka-math.org
G1-M3-TE-BK3-1.3.1-01.2016

EUREKA
MATH

3. Use all of the fish measurements to complete the sentences.

   a. Fish A is longer than Fish _____ and shorter than Fish _____.

   b. Fish C is shorter than Fish _____ and longer than Fish _____.

   c. Fish _____ is the shortest fish.

   d. If Natasha gets a new fish that is shorter than Fish A, list the fish that the new fish is also shorter than.

Use your centimeter cubes to model each length, and answer the question.

4. Henry gets a new pencil that is 19 centimeters long. He sharpens the pencil several times. If the pencil is now 9 centimeters long, how much shorter is the pencil now than when it was new?

5. Malik and Jared each found a stick at the park. Malik found a stick that was 11 centimeters long. Jared found a stick that was 17 centimeters long. How much longer was Jared's stick?

Lesson 6:   Order, measure, and compare the length of objects before and after measuring with centimeter cubes, solving *compare with difference unknown* word problems.

97

© 2015 Great Minds. eureka-math.org
G1-M3-TE-BK3-1.3.1-01.2016

Topic C

Non-Standard and Standard Length Units

1.OA.1, 1.MD.2

Focus Standards:	1.OA.1		Use addition and subtraction within 20 to solve word problems involving situations of adding to, taking from, putting together, taking apart, and comparing, with unknowns in all positions, e.g., by using objects, drawings, and equations with a symbol for the unknown number to represent the problem.
	1.MD.2		Express the length of an object as a whole number of length units, by laying multiple copies of a shorter object (the length unit) end to end; understand that the length measurement of an object is the number of same-size length units that span it with no gaps or overlaps. *Limit to contexts where the object being measured is spanned by a whole number of length units with no gaps or overlaps.*
Instructional Days:	3		
Coherence	-Links from:	GK–M3	Comparison of Length, Weight, Capacity, and Numbers to 10
	-Links to:	G2–M2	Addition and Subtraction of Length Units
		G2–M7	Problem Solving with Length, Money, and Data

Topic C gives students a chance to explore the usefulness of measuring with similar units. The topic opens with Lesson 7 where students measure the same objects from Topic B using two different non-standard length units simultaneously, such as toothpicks and small paper clips (**1.MD.2**). They then use small paper clips and large paper clips, two non-standard units that happen to be the same object but different lengths. Each time they measure one object using both units, they receive inconsistent measurement results. Students then begin to ask the question, "Why do we measure with same-sized length units?" As they explore why it is so important to use the same-sized length unit, they realize that doing so yields consistent measurement results.

In Lesson 8, students explore what happens when they use a different unit of measurement from that of their classmates. As students measure the same objects with different non-standard length units, they realize that in order to have discussions about the lengths of objects, they *must* measure with the same units. Students answer the question, "If Bailey uses paper clips and Maya uses toothpicks, and they both measure things in our classroom, will they be able to compare their measurements?" With this new understanding of consistent measurement, Lesson 9 closes the topic with students solving *compare with difference unknown* problems using centimeter cubes. Students explore and solve problems such as, "How much longer is the pencil than the marker?" (**1.OA.1**). Revisiting the centimeter helps students recognize the value of having a consistent way to communicate about various measurements.

A Teaching Sequence Toward Mastery of Non-Standard and Standard Length Units

Objective 1: Measure the same objects from Topic B with different non-standard units simultaneously to see the need to measure with a consistent unit.
(Lesson 7)

Objective 2: Understand the need to use the same units when comparing measurements with others.
(Lesson 8)

Objective 3: Answer *compare with difference unknown* problems about lengths of two different objects measured in centimeters.
(Lesson 9)

Lesson 7

Objective: Measure the same objects from Topic B with different non-standard units simultaneously to see the need to measure with a consistent unit.

Suggested Lesson Structure

■ Fluency Practice   (18 minutes)
■ Application Problem   (5 minutes)
■ Concept Development   (27 minutes)
■ Student Debrief   (10 minutes)
  Total Time   **(60 minutes)**

Fluency Practice (18 minutes)

▪ Beep Counting **1.NBT.1**   (2 minutes)
▪ Addition Strategies Review **1.OA.6**   (6 minutes)
▪ Sprint: Addition Within 20 **1.OA.6**   (10 minutes)

Beep Counting (2 minutes)

Note: This fluency activity strengthens students' ability to understand number relationships and to recognize counting patterns. If students are proficient with beep counting by ones, consider beep counting by tens (**1.NBT.5**) or practicing the Grade 2 standard of counting by twos or fives (**2.NBT.2**).

Say a series of three or more numbers, but replace one of the numbers with the word *beep* (e.g., 15, 16, beep). When signaled, students say the number that was replaced by the word *beep* in the sequence. Scaffold number sequences, beginning with easy sequences and moving to more complex ones. Be sure to include forward and backward number sequences and to change the sequential placement of the beep.

Suggested sequence: 15, 16, beep; 25, 26, beep; 35, 36, beep; 12, 11, beep; 22, 21, beep; 32, 31, beep; 8, beep, 10; 18, beep, 20; 38, beep, 40; beep, 9, 8; beep, 19, 18; and beep, 29, 28.

EUREKA
MATH

Addition Strategies Review (6 minutes)

Materials: (T) Hide Zero cards (Lesson 2 Fluency Template 1)

Note: This review fluency activity helps strengthen students' understanding of the make ten and add the ones addition strategies. It also strengthens their ability to recognize appropriate strategies based on the number of tens and ones in both addends.

T: (Divide students into partnerships. Show 9 and 6 with Hide Zero cards.) Partner A, show me 9 on your Magic Counting Sticks. Partner B, show me 6. If I want to solve 9 + 6, how can I make a ten?

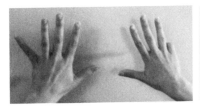 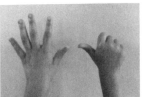

S: Take 1 from the 6, and add 1 to 9.

T: Yes. Show me! (Exchange the 9 and 6 cards for 10 and 5 as students adjust their fingers.) We changed 9 + 6 into an easier problem. Say our new addition sentence with the solution.

S: 10 + 5 = 15.

T: (Put the Hide Zero cards together to show 15.) Say it the Say Ten way.

S: Ten 5.

T: (Show 13 with Hide Zero cards.) Partner A, show the ones. Partner B, show the tens. (Break apart the Hide Zero cards as students hold up their fingers.) If we want to add 2, should we make a ten to help us?

S: No. We already have a ten!

T: Should we add 2 to our 3 or our 10?

S: Our 3.

T: Yes! Partner A, show me 3 + 2. (Exchange the 3 card for a 5 card.) What is the answer?

S: 5.

T: So, Partner B, what is 13 + 2?

S: 15.

T: Say it the Say Ten way

S: Ten 5.

Sprint: Addition Within 20 (10 minutes)

Materials: (S) Addition Within 20 Sprint

Note: This Sprint addresses the Grade 1 standard of adding and subtracting within 20.

Application Problem (5 minutes)

When Corey measures his new pencil, he uses 19 centimeter cubes. After he sharpens the pencil, he needs 4 fewer centimeter cubes. How long is Corey's pencil after he sharpens it? Use centimeter cubes to solve the problem. Write a number sentence and a statement to answer the question.

Note: As students build measurements with centimeter cubes, they continue to connect their experiences of addition and subtraction with concrete problem situations. As students work, encourage them to talk through the problem sentence by sentence, placing the centimeter cubes in front of them to build the story.

During the Student Debrief, connect students' concrete experience with the problem type or computation.

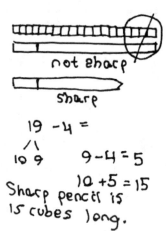

Concept Development (27 minutes)

Materials: (T) Chart paper, 3 new pencils of different colors (e.g., red, blue, yellow) from the same brand and size, mixed set of large and small paper clips
(S) Bag of 20 large paper clips and 20 small paper clips

Note: The chart created during today's lesson is used throughout the remainder of the module.

Gather students in the meeting area with their materials.

T: For the past few days, we have been measuring with centimeter cubes. Today, let's measure with paper clips. What did we learn about the rules of measuring? (Write the rules on chart paper as students respond. Model how to measure objects that are longer or shorter than a whole unit. Discuss how best to choose the number of units when estimating.)

S: Line up the endpoints. → Don't leave any gaps. → Don't overlap what you are measuring with.

T: Let's see how long this red pencil is by using paper clips as our length unit. (Measure with a mix of both paper clips, e.g., 3 large and 1 small.) How many paper clips long is the red pencil?

S: 4 paper clips long.

> **A NOTE ON
> MULTIPLE MEANS
> OF REPRESENTATION:**
>
> Ask questions to guide connections, analysis, and mastery of concepts. This allows students the opportunity to develop critical thinking skills instead of just memorizing answers.

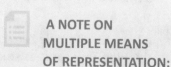

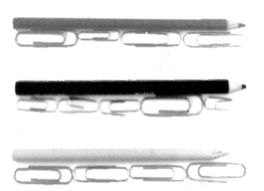

Lesson 7:   Measure the same objects from Topic B with different non-standard units simultaneously to see the need to measure with a consistent unit.

**EUREKA
MATH**

T: (Keep the red pencil measurement displayed.) This blue pencil is the same length. Let's measure it using paper clips as the length unit. (Measure with a different combination of paper clips, e.g., 1 large and 4 small.) How many paper clips long is the blue pencil?

S: 5 paper clips long.

T: According to these measurements, the blue pencil is longer than the red. Is this correct?

S: Yes. → But, it looks like the pencils are the same length!

T: Let's compare the pencils directly. (Pick up the pencils from their places, and stand them up from the floor. Leave the paper clip measurements where they are.) Are they the same length?

S: Yes!

T: (Put the pencils back so they are aligned with their paper clips.)

T: Hmmm. Let me measure again. This yellow pencil is also the same length as the others. (Measure with a different combination of paper clips, e.g., 4 large paper clips.) Oh boy, this time, it's *less* than 4 paper clips long! Why do I keep getting different measurements when the pencils are the same size?

T: I'm using the length unit of a paper clip. (Refer to the chart with measuring rules.) I'm aligning my endpoints, making sure there are no gaps or overlaps. I should be getting the same length measurement each time since the pencils are the same length.

T: Talk to your partner. Can you figure out what I need to change about the way I'm measuring?

MP.3

S: The paper clips are different sizes! → Some paper clips are long and others are short! → It's not an accurate measurement because the paper clips have to be the same size, just like our centimeter cubes were the same size, a centimeter. → We should only use the smaller paper clips. → Or, we should only use the bigger paper clips. But, we can't mix them.

T: It sounds to me like we have a new rule for proper measuring! (Add to the chart: *Length units must be the same length.*) Just like you said, we need to make a decision: either use just the small paper clips or…?

S: Just the big paper clips!

T: Great. And what should we make sure we don't do?

S: Don't mix them up because they are different sizes!

T: (Ask a student volunteer to come up and use small paper clips to measure the red pencil. Measure the blue pencil with small paper clips as the student measures the red pencil.) How many paper clips long is the blue pencil? How many paper clips long is the red pencil?

S: They are both about 6 small paper clips long!

T: Thank you for solving my measurement problem! You're ready to measure with paper clips on your Problem Set. First, let's read all of our rules for measuring.

While distributing a bag of varying paper clips to each student, remind the class of the new rule to make sure they use the same length paper clips as they measure. (Note: It would be helpful to students to have the chart hanging in the classroom for future reference.)

NOTES ON MULTIPLE MEANS OF ENGAGEMENT:

Provide challenging extensions for students who are able to measure more complex objects. Provide them with an object to be measured both horizontally and vertically, and find the difference. Students can also measure something round using a tape measure. Have them present their findings to the class.

Lesson 7: Measure the same objects from Topic B with different non-standard units simultaneously to see the need to measure with a consistent unit.

103

Problem Set (10 minutes)

Students should do their personal best to complete the Problem Set within the allotted 10 minutes. For some classes, it may be appropriate to modify the assignment by specifying which problems they work on first.

Note: Circulate to ensure that students use the correct size paper clip for each set of questions. The last two items on the chart are found in the classroom, not on the Problem Set.

Student Debrief (10 minutes)

Lesson Objective: Measure the same objects from Topic B with different non-standard units simultaneously to see the need to measure with a consistent unit.

The Student Debrief is intended to invite reflection and active processing of the total lesson experience.

Invite students to review their solutions for the Problem Set. They should check work by comparing answers with a partner before going over answers as a class. Look for misconceptions or misunderstandings that can be addressed in the Debrief. Guide students in a conversation to debrief the Problem Set and process the lesson.

Any combination of the questions below may be used to lead the discussion.

- What is a new rule we must remember when we are measuring?
- Compare your first chart to your partner's. Explain why you have the same measurements.
- Even though we measured the same objects, why are your measurements different on your first chart than on your second chart?
- A student said she used new pencil-top erasers from a pack to measure how long her pencil is. All the erasers are the same size. Her partner said she couldn't use these erasers to measure properly because they are all different colors. Who is correct? Explain your thinking.
- Look at your Application Problem. What measurement rules did you have to keep in mind? Did you add more cubes or take cubes away to solve this problem? What number sentence matches the problem?

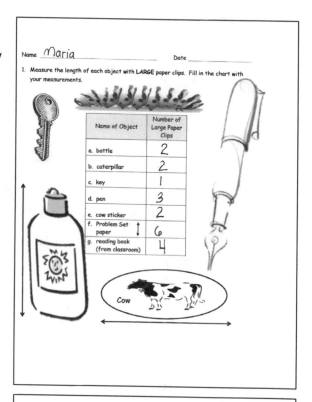

Name Maria _____   Date _____

1. Measure the length of each object with **LARGE** paper clips. Fill in the chart with your measurements.

Name of Object	Number of Large Paper Clips
a. bottle	2
b. caterpillar	2
c. key	1
d. pen	3
e. cow sticker	2
f. Problem Set paper	6
g. reading book (from classroom)	4

Cow

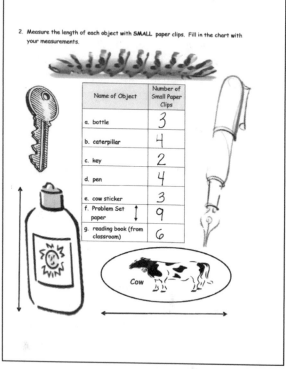

2. Measure the length of each object with **SMALL** paper clips. Fill in the chart with your measurements.

Name of Object	Number of Small Paper Clips
a. bottle	3
b. caterpillar	4
c. key	2
d. pen	4
e. cow sticker	3
f. Problem Set paper	9
g. reading book (from classroom)	6

Cow

Lesson 7: Measure the same objects from Topic B with different non-standard units simultaneously to see the need to measure with a consistent unit.

EUREKA MATH

Exit Ticket (3 minutes)

After the Student Debrief, instruct students to complete the Exit Ticket. A review of their work will help with assessing students' understanding of the concepts that were presented in today's lesson and planning more effectively for future lessons. The questions may be read aloud to the students.

Lesson 7:   Measure the same objects from Topic B with different non-standard units simultaneously to see the need to measure with a consistent unit.

105

© 2015 Great Minds. eureka-math.org
G1-M3-TE-BK3-1.3.1-01.2016

A

Name _____

Number Correct: _____

Date _____

*Write the missing number.

1.	$17 + 1 = \square$		16.	$11 + 9 = \square$	
2.	$15 + 1 = \square$		17.	$10 + 9 = \square$	
3.	$18 + 1 = \square$		18.	$9 + 9 = \square$	
4.	$15 + 2 = \square$		19.	$7 + 9 = \square$	
5.	$17 + 2 = \square$		20.	$8 + 8 = \square$	
6.	$18 + 2 = \square$		21.	$7 + 8 = \square$	
7.	$15 + 3 = \square$		22.	$8 + 5 = \square$	
8.	$5 + 13 = \square$		23.	$11 + 8 = \square$	
9.	$15 + 2 = \square$		24.	$12 + \square = 17$	
10.	$5 + 12 = \square$		25.	$14 + \square = 17$	
11.	$12 + 4 = \square$		26.	$8 + \square = 17$	
12.	$13 + 4 = \square$		27.	$\square + 7 = 16$	
13.	$3 + 14 = \square$		28.	$\square + 7 = 15$	
14.	$17 + 2 = \square$		29.	$9 + 5 = 10 + \square$	
15.	$12 + 7 = \square$		30.	$7 + 8 = \square + 9$	

Lesson 7:   Measure the same objects from Topic B with different non-standard units simultaneously to see the need to measure with a consistent unit.

EUREKA MATH

B

Number Correct: _____

Name _____

Date _____

*Write the missing number.

1.	$14 + 1 = \square$		16.	$11 + 9 = \square$	
2.	$16 + 1 = \square$		17.	$10 + 9 = \square$	
3.	$17 + 1 = \square$		18.	$8 + 9 = \square$	
4.	$11 + 2 = \square$		19.	$9 + 9 = \square$	
5.	$15 + 2 = \square$		20.	$9 + 8 = \square$	
6.	$17 + 2 = \square$		21.	$8 + 8 = \square$	
7.	$15 + 4 = \square$		22.	$8 + 5 = \square$	
8.	$4 + 15 = \square$		23.	$11 + 7 = \square$	
9.	$15 + 3 = \square$		24.	$12 + \square = 18$	
10.	$5 + 13 = \square$		25.	$14 + \square = 18$	
11.	$13 + 4 = \square$		26.	$8 + \square = 18$	
12.	$14 + 4 = \square$		27.	$\square + 5 = 14$	
13.	$4 + 14 = \square$		28.	$\square + 6 = 15$	
14.	$16 + 3 = \square$		29.	$9 + 6 = 10 + \square$	
15.	$13 + 6 = \square$		30.	$6 + 7 = \square + 9$	

EUREKA MATH®

© 2015 Great Minds. eureka-math.org
G1-M3-TE-BK3-1.3.1-01.2016

Name _____   Date _____

1. Measure the length of each object with **LARGE** paper clips. Fill in the chart with
    your measurements.

Name of Object	Number of Large Paper Clips
a. bottle	
b. caterpillar	
c. key	
d. pen	
e. cow sticker	
f. Problem Set paper	
g. reading book (from classroom)	

Cow

Lesson 7: Measure the same objects from Topic B with different non-standard
units simultaneously to see the need to measure with a consistent
unit.

© 2015 Great Minds. eureka-math.org
G1-M3-TE-BK3-1.3.1-01.2016

EUREKA
MATH

2. Measure the length of each object with **SMALL** paper clips. Fill in the chart with your measurements.

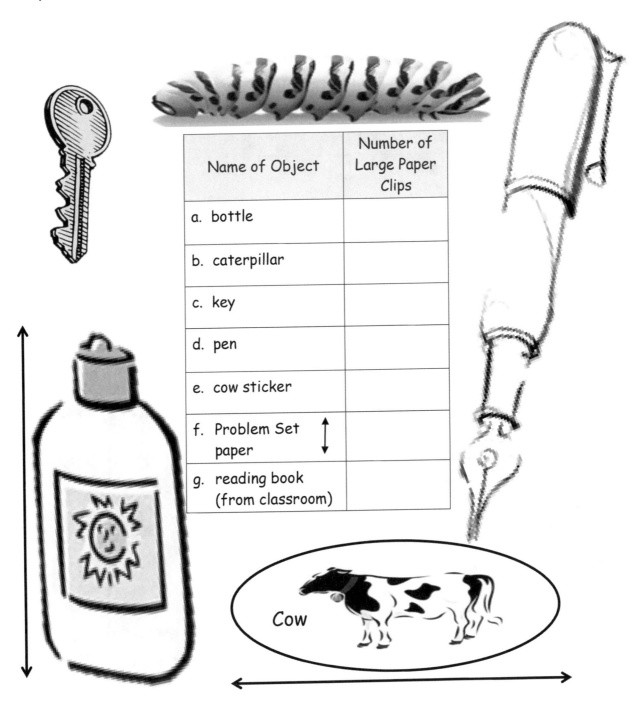

Name of Object	Number of Large Paper Clips
a. bottle	
b. caterpillar	
c. key	
d. pen	
e. cow sticker	
f. Problem Set paper	
g. reading book (from classroom)	

Cow

Lesson 7: Measure the same objects from Topic B with different non-standard units simultaneously to see the need to measure with a consistent unit.

109

Name _____ Date _____

Measure the length of each object with **large** paper clips. Then, measure the length of each object with **small** paper clips. Fill in the chart with your measurements.

Name of Object	Number of Large Paper Clips	Number of Small Paper Clips
a. bow		
b. candle		
c. vase and flowers		

Lesson 7:   Measure the same objects from Topic B with different non-standard units simultaneously to see the need to measure with a consistent unit.

© 2015 Great Minds. eureka-math.org
G1-M3-TE-BK3-1.3.1-01.2016

EUREKA
MATH®

Name _____ Date _____

Cut the strip of paper clips. Measure the length of each object with the **large** paper clips to the right. Then, measure the length with the **small** paper clips on the back.

1. Fill in the chart on the back of the page with your measurements.

Paintbrush

Scissors

Glue

Crayon

Eraser

Lesson 7: Measure the same objects from Topic B with different non-standard units simultaneously to see the need to measure with a consistent unit.

111

Name of Object	Length in Large Paper Clips	Length in Small Paper Clips
a. paintbrush		
b. scissors		
c. eraser		
d. crayon		
e. glue		

2. Find objects around your home to measure. Record the objects you find and their measurements on the chart.

Name of Object	Length in Large Paper Clips	Length in Small Paper Clips
a.		
b.		
c.		
d.		
e.		

Lesson 7:   Measure the same objects from Topic B with different non-standard units simultaneously to see the need to measure with a consistent unit.

Lesson 8

Objective: Understand the need to use the same units when comparing measurements with others.

Suggested Lesson Structure

■ Fluency Practice	(10 minutes)	
■ Application Problem	(5 minutes)	
■ Concept Development	(35 minutes)	
■ Student Debrief	(10 minutes)	
Total Time	**(60 minutes)**	

Fluency Practice (10 minutes)

- Speed Writing **1.OA.5**   (3 minutes)
- Race and Roll Addition **1.OA.6**   (4 minutes)
- Cold Call: Addition and Subtraction Within 20 **1.OA.6**   (3 minutes)

Speed Writing (3 minutes)

Materials: (T) Timer (S) Personal white board

Note: Throughout the first two modules, students have been counting by ones, twos, fives, and tens, as well as the Say Ten way.

Review of these counting patterns prepares students for Module 4 by strengthening their understanding of place value and their ability to add and subtract. Many students are familiar with skip-counting. Though skip-counting by twos, fives, and tens is not a Grade 1 standard, the teacher can incorporate these counting patterns, if appropriate.

Choose a counting pattern with which students need more practice. Students count on their boards by the chosen pattern for one minute. Tell them to erase their boards but to remember how high they counted. Then, give them another minute to try to count even higher.

**NOTES ON
MULTIPLE MEANS
OF REPRESENTATION:**

If there are students who are unable to count by the chosen pattern without numerical visual cues at this point in the year, use a tool such as a number line or a hundreds chart. Students can color the pattern on the number line or hundreds chart so that they have a visual representation as they count on their own.

EUREKA
MATH

Lesson 8:   Understand the need to use the same units when comparing
                  measurements with others.

113

Race and Roll Addition (4 minutes)

Materials: (S) 1 die per pair

Note: This fluency activity reviews the grade level standard of adding within 20.

Partners start at 0. Partners take turns rolling a die and then saying a number sentence by adding the number rolled to the total. (For example, Partner A rolls 6 and says, "0 + 6 = 6." Partner B rolls 3 and says, "6 + 3 = 9.") They continue rapidly rolling and saying number sentences until they get to 20, without going over. (For example, if partners are at 18 and roll 5, they take turns rolling until one of them rolls 2 or 1 two times.) Partners stand when they reach 20.

Cold Call: Addition and Subtraction Within 20 (3 minutes)

Note: This review fluency activity addresses the Grade 1 standard of adding and subtracting within 20 and practices including units when adding length.

For directions on how to play Cold Call, refer to Lesson 6.

   T: 4 centimeters + 2 centimeters is…? (Pause to provide think time.) Only students with pets answer. Ready?

   S: (Only students with pets answer.) 6 centimeters.

   T: 14 centimeters + 2 centimeters is…? (Pause to provide think time.) Only students without pets answer. Ready?

   S: (Only students with no pets answer.) 16 centimeters.

Continue playing, practicing addition and subtraction within 20. As always, scaffold instruction by beginning with easy problems and slowly increasing the complexity.

Application Problem (5 minutes)

I have 2 crayons. Each crayon is 9 centimeter cubes long. I also have a paintbrush. The paintbrush is the same length as 2 crayons. How many centimeter cubes long is the paintbrush? Use centimeter cubes to solve the problem. Then, draw a picture, and write a number sentence and a statement to answer the question.

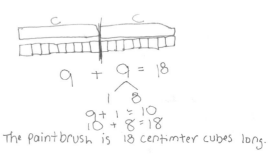

Note: Students continue to use concrete materials to consider problem situations. Continue to encourage students to build each part of the story, using the cubes to think through what they know and to identify what they do not yet know. During the Student Debrief, students demonstrate their strategies for solving the problem. The example above shows one way in which students may solve this Application Problem. Some students may simply align the cubes and solve without drawing.

114   Lesson 8:   Understand the need to use the same units when comparing
                              measurements with others.

© 2015 Great Minds. eureka-math.org
G1-M3-TE-BK3-1.3.1-01.2016

EUREKA
MATH

Concept Development (35 minutes)

Materials: (T) Chart with measuring rules (Lesson 7) (S) 1 lunch bag of 2 new crayons, 10 linking cubes, and 10 centimeter cubes per pair

Gather students in the meeting area in a semicircle.

T: We have measured with many different tools so far. Who can name the different tools we have used to measure?

S: String. → Strip of paper (or pipe cleaners). → Centimeter cubes. → Centimeter ruler. →Small paper clips. → Large paper clips.

Review the rules for measuring properly using the chart created in Lesson 7.

T: (Distribute a lunch bag with materials listed above to each pair of students.) Take the materials out of your bag. You and your partner are going to measure the new crayons with the other materials in your bag. Don't forget about the rules for proper measuring!

T: The new crayon is how many cubes long? (Note: Do not tell students which cubes to use.)

S: Mine was 9 cubes long. → Mine was 3 cubes long.

T: That's interesting. These crayons are brand new, and they came from the same box, which means they should be the same size. (Match up the crayons.) And they are! Why are we getting different measurements?

Ask students if they measured properly by going over each rule, repeating the last rule twice to ensure that no one mixed the cubes to measure.

MP.6

T: Why do we have different measurements? Talk with your partner.

S: We were measuring with different cubes. We didn't mix them up, but I measured with smaller cubes, the centimeter cubes. My partner measured with bigger cubes, the linking cubes. → We didn't do anything wrong. We measured correctly. It's just that our answers are different because we each used a different size cube to measure.

T: Great thinking! Even though you measured properly, it sounds like we need to add a rule for *sharing and communicating* about our measurements. When someone says, "My crayon is 3 cubes long," and another person says, "No! It's 9 cubes long," this can become a frustrating conversation because they are both right! So, how can we help these two students?

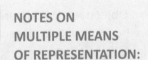

**NOTES ON
MULTIPLE MEANS
OF REPRESENTATION:**

Highlight vocabulary that could be unfamiliar for English language learners. Vocabulary in this lesson that might be highlighted is *sharing* and *communicating*. Provide some examples of how students share and communicate outside of math so they can make the connection.

S: They have to say, "My crayon is 3 *linking* cubes long," or "My crayon is 9 *centimeter* cubes long." → We have to say what type of tool we used to measure!

T: Yes! We need to be precise when we communicate about which length unit we used to measure. Practice measuring more items and communicating their measurements precisely on your Problem Set.

    Lesson 8:   Understand the need to use the same units when comparing measurements with others.

115

© 2015 Great Minds. eureka-math.org
G1-M3-TE-BK3-1.3.1-01.2016

Give each student, or pair of students, *one* set of the following measuring tools:

- 20 small paper clips
- 20 large paper clips
- 20 toothpicks
- 20 centimeter cubes

Ask students to measure the classroom objects with their assigned measuring tools. Remind students to write the word *about* if their measurement is not exactly a certain length unit long. Circulate and ask students about their measurements, encouraging them to use the length unit label as they share. (Note: The use of the word *about* was first introduced in Lesson 4. Remind students that if they are going to use this word, the appropriate way to use it is, for example, "My pretzel rod is about 18 centimeter cubes long.")

Problem Set (10 minutes)

Students should do their personal best to complete the Problem Set within the allotted 10 minutes. For some classes, it may be appropriate to modify the assignment by specifying which problems they work on first.

For the Problem Set and Homework, each student gets *one* of the following: bag of 20 small paper clips, bag of 20 large paper clips, bag of 20 toothpicks, or bag of 20 centimeter cubes. Be sure to have each student take the bag home to complete the Homework assignment.

Student Debrief (10 minutes)

Lesson Objective: Understand the need to use the same units when comparing measurements with others.

The Student Debrief is intended to invite reflection and active processing of the total lesson experience.

Invite students to review their solutions for the Problem Set. They should check work by comparing answers with a partner who used the same length unit before going over answers as a class. Look for misconceptions or misunderstandings that can be addressed in the Debrief. Guide students in a conversation to debrief the Problem Set and process the lesson.

Any combination of the questions below may be used to lead the discussion.

- Compare your measurements to your partner's (a student who used a different tool). How are your answers different?
- Why do we need a label, or a length unit, along with a number when we are writing our measurements? Why can't we use the number only?

Lesson 8: Understand the need to use the same units when comparing measurements with others.

- How can it be true that when Student A says the glue stick is X paper clips long and Student B says it is Y centimeter cubes long, they are both correct?

- Student A says she used 9 centimeter cubes to measure the crayon. Student B says she used 3 small paper clips to measure the crayon. Why do you think she needed so many more centimeter cubes to measure the crayon compared to using the small paper clips?

- Pick three objects from your sheet. Name your items in order from shortest to longest. Name your items in order from longest to shortest.

- Would the order change if you were using a different measuring tool to measure length? Why or why not?

- Display an example of the Problem Set for Lesson 7. Look at the caterpillar on each page. How do our measurements on each page relate to today's lesson?

- Look at your Application Problem. How much longer is the paintbrush compared to one crayon? Why is it important that you included the label *centimeters* or *centimeter cubes* after the number in your statement?

Exit Ticket (3 minutes)

After the Student Debrief, instruct students to complete the Exit Ticket. A review of their work will help with assessing students' understanding of the concepts that were presented in today's lesson and planning more effectively for future lessons. The questions may be read aloud to the students.

Lesson 8: Understand the need to use the same units when comparing measurements with others.

© 2015 Great Minds. eureka-math.org
G1-M3-TE-BK3-1.3.1-01.2016

117

Name _____ Date _____

Circle the length unit you will use to measure. Use the same length unit for all objects.

Small Paper Clips

Large Paper Clips

Toothpicks

Centimeter Cubes

Measure each object listed on the chart, and record the measurement. Add the names of other objects in the classroom, and record their measurements.

Classroom Object	Measurement
a. glue stick	
b. dry erase marker	
c. unsharpened pencil	
d. personal white board	
e.	
f.	
g.	

Lesson 8:   Understand the need to use the same units when comparing measurements with others.

Name _____   Date _____

Circle the length unit you will use to measure. Use the same length unit for all objects.

Small Paper Clips

Large Paper Clips

Toothpicks

Centimeter Cubes

Choose two objects in your desk that you would like to measure. Measure each object, and record the measurement.

Classroom Object	Measurement
a.	
b.	

Lesson 8:   Understand the need to use the same units when comparing
measurements with others.

119

© 2015 Great Minds. eureka-math.org
G1-M3-TE-BK3-1.3.1-01.2016

Name _____   Date _____

Circle the length unit you will use to measure. Use the same length unit for all objects.

Small Paper Clips

Large Paper Clips

Toothpicks

Centimeter Cubes

1. Measure each object listed on the chart, and record the measurement. Add the names of other objects in your house, and record their measurements.

Home Object	Measurement
a. fork	
b. picture frame	
c. pan	
d. shoe	

Lesson 8:   Understand the need to use the same units when comparing
measurements with others.

EUREKA
MATH

Home Object	Measurement
e. stuffed animal	
f.	
g.	

Did you remember to add the name of the length unit after the number? Yes   No

2. Pick 3 items from the chart. List your items from longest to shortest:

a. _____

b. _____

c. _____

Lesson 8: Understand the need to use the same units when comparing measurements with others.

121

Lesson 9

Objective: Answer *compare with difference unknown* problems about lengths of two different objects measured in centimeters.

Suggested Lesson Structure

- ■ Fluency Practice   (18 minutes)
- ■ Application Problem   (5 minutes)
- ■ Concept Development   (27 minutes)
- ■ Student Debrief   (10 minutes)
  - **Total Time**   **(60 minutes)**

Fluency Practice (18 minutes)

- Race and Roll Addition **1.OA.6**   (5 minutes)
- Sprint: Addition Within 20 **1.OA.6**   (10 minutes)
- Number Sentence Swap **1.OA.4**   (3 minutes)

Race and Roll Addition (5 minutes)

Materials: (S) 1 die per pair

Note: This fluency activity reviews the grade level standard of adding within 20.

Partners start at 0. Partners take turns rolling a die and then saying a number sentence by adding the number rolled to the total. (For example, Partner A rolls 6 and says, "0 + 6 = 6." Partner B rolls 3 and says, "6 + 3 = 9.") They continue rapidly rolling and saying number sentences until they get to 20, without going over. (For example, if partners are at 18 and roll 5, they take turns rolling until one of them rolls 2 or 1 two times.) Partners stand when they reach 20.

Sprint: Addition Within 20 (10 minutes)

Materials: (S) Addition Within 20 Sprint

Note: This Sprint addresses the Grade 1 standard of adding and subtracting within 20. It is the same Sprint from Lesson 7, so students will likely do better today. Along with celebrating improvement between Sides A and B, celebrate improvement from the last time this Sprint was given.

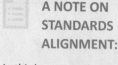

> **A NOTE ON STANDARDS ALIGNMENT:**
>
> In this lesson, students compare centimeter cubes as a concrete form of *compare with difference unknown* problem types. This bridges toward the Grade 2 standard of measuring to determine how much longer one object is than another (**2.MD.4**), although the lesson specifically focuses on comparing the concrete cubes rather than the more abstract numerical representations of the measurements.

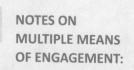

> **NOTES ON MULTIPLE MEANS OF ENGAGEMENT:**
>
> While some students thrive during Sprints, others may not enjoy having to complete a timed task. Cultivate healthy *personal best* competition during Sprints so that students focus on their improvement.

Lesson 9:   Answer *compare with difference unknown* problems about lengths of two different objects measured in centimeters.

EUREKA MATH

Number Sentence Swap (3 minutes)

Say a subtraction sentence aloud, saying "the mystery number" for the unknown answer (e.g., 5 – 3 = the mystery number). Call on a student to rephrase the sentence as an addition sentence (e.g., 3 + the mystery number = 5). Pause to provide think time. Students solve for the mystery number at the signal.

Continue with the following suggested sequence: 5 – 3, 15 – 3, 6 – 4, and 16 – 4.

Application Problem (5 minutes)

Corey buys a super-cool, extra-long crayon that is 14 centimeters long. His regular crayon is 9 centimeters long. Use centimeter cubes to find out how much longer Corey's new crayon is than his regular crayon.

Write a statement to answer the question.
Write a number sentence to show what you did.

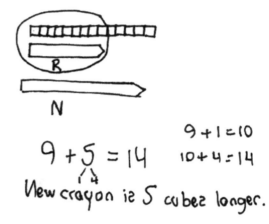

Note: This problem continues to provide students with opportunities to concretely build various lengths with centimeter cubes. As students work toward solving *compare with difference unknown* problem types, experiences with concrete objects like centimeter cubes can strengthen understanding. Students explore the comparison of centimeter cubes during today's lesson. As students work, notice how they are solving, and use your analysis during the Concept Development.

Concept Development (27 minutes)

Materials: (T) 2 different colors of centimeter cubes (e.g., blue and yellow), dry erase marker, jumbo craft stick, crayon, glue stick, small paper clip, unsharpened pencil, new colored pencil, chart with measuring rules (Lesson 7) (S) Bag with 20 blue and 20 yellow centimeter cubes, bag with classroom materials (Lesson 4), new colored pencil

Note: Adjust the Concept Development as necessary based on observations of student successes and challenges during Lesson 6, as well as during the most recent Application Problems. Today's Concept Development is an opportunity to continue supporting student understanding of the *compare with difference unknown* problem types within the concrete context of comparing lengths of centimeter cubes. As addressed in the Note on Standards Alignment, the focus of the lesson should be on comparing the cubes themselves rather than the Grade 2 standard of comparing the measurements alone.

Gather students in the meeting area in a semicircle formation.

   T: (Post the chart with measuring rules from Lesson 7.) The teacher next door and I were playing a game. Whoever found the longer object on our desks won, but the object could not be longer than a new pencil. For each extra centimeter in length, the person with the longer object got a point.

Lesson 9:   Answer *compare with difference unknown* problems about lengths of two different objects measured in centimeters.

123

© 2015 Great Minds. eureka-math.org
G1-M3-TE-BK3-1.3.1-01.2016

T: The teacher next door found a craft stick, and I found a dry erase marker, just like the ones on our chart (point to the chart). My dry erase marker measured 12 centimeters, and his craft stick measured 15 centimeters. He said he got 15 points, but I don't think that's right. Let's lay the centimeter cubes down and compare them to see how many points he should have gotten in our game.

T: I have 12 centimeter cubes here in my hand. (Lay the two objects in the middle. Point to the chart.) The dry erase marker is 12 centimeters long. Will I have enough cubes to measure my dry erase marker?

S: Yes! It is 12 centimeters long, and you have 12 centimeter cubes.

T: (Lay down blue centimeter cubes along the dry erase marker. Point to the craft stick measurement of 15 centimeters on the chart.) Will these same 12 cubes be enough to measure the craft stick?

S: No! There are only 12 centimeter cubes. The craft stick is 15 centimeters long.

T: (Lay down 12 blue centimeter cubes along the craft stick.) The teacher next door said he should get 15 points because it took 15 more centimeter cubes to measure the craft stick than the marker! Look at the marker and the centimeter cubes we laid down. Is he right? Did he need 15 more cubes along with the 12 cubes I needed? Talk with a partner. How many more cubes did the teacher next door need compared to the number of cubes I used? (Have partners share their thinking with the class.)

T: Now, let's try the other teacher's idea. (Add 15 more cubes, this time using yellow cubes.) Wow, this is too long! It's much longer than the difference between what he already has and what he needs. What should I do?

S: Take away all of the extra cubes until they line up with the end of the craft stick.

T: (Three yellow cubes are left.) So, if I had 12 cubes and he had 15 cubes, how many more cubes did the teacher need compared to me?

S: 3 more cubes.

MP.2

T: How much longer is the teacher's craft stick compared to my marker?

S: 3 centimeters.

T: How much shorter is my marker compared to the teacher's craft stick?

S: 3 centimeters.

T: So, for that round, the teacher got 3 points because his stick was 3 centimeters longer than my marker. The teacher tried to get 15 points for that one, but I'm glad we figured out that he only gets 3 points.

Repeat the process by having students work with their centimeter cubes, measuring using the following contexts. Model as much as appropriate.

- Measure a new colored pencil and an unsharpened pencil as in the game between the two teachers.

- Students measure and compare the lengths of a crayon and a glue stick to see which item is shorter and by how much.

NOTES ON MULTIPLE MEANS OF REPRESENTATION:

Reading word problems aloud facilitates problem solving for those students who have difficulty reading the text. Make sure students with reading difficulties are not held back by the reading when they are able to solve the math problems.

Lesson 9:   Answer *compare with difference unknown* problems about lengths of two different objects measured in centimeters.

EUREKA MATH

- Kelly is knitting a scarf for her doll. It needs to be 13 centimeters long. She has already knitted 9 centimeters. How many more centimeters need to be knitted?

Problem Set (10 minutes)

Students should do their personal best to complete the Problem Set within the allotted 10 minutes. For some classes, it may be appropriate to modify the assignment by specifying which problems they work on first.

Note: For the Problem Set, students use actual centimeter cubes to solve the problems.

Student Debrief (10 minutes)

Lesson Objective: Answer *compare with difference unknown* problems about lengths of two different objects measured in centimeters.

The Student Debrief is intended to invite reflection and active processing of the total lesson experience.

Invite students to review their solutions for the Problem Set. They should check work by comparing answers with a partner before going over answers as a class. Look for misconceptions or misunderstandings that can be addressed in the Debrief. Guide students in a conversation to debrief the Problem Set and process the lesson.

Any combination of the questions below may be used to lead the discussion.

- Look at Problems 3 and 4. What do you notice about the answers? Explain to your partner why this is so.
- Look at Problem 8. Can you think of a number sentence that can help you check your answer?
- What strategy helped you when you tried to find the difference between two objects?
- Look at today's Application Problem. How does it apply to today's lesson?

Note: Send the bags of centimeter cubes home with students for use in completing their homework.

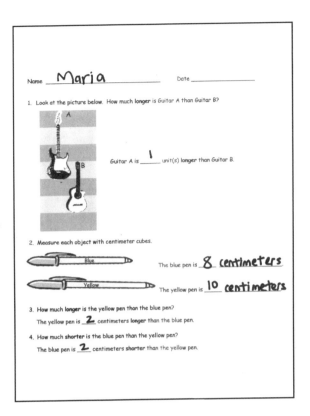

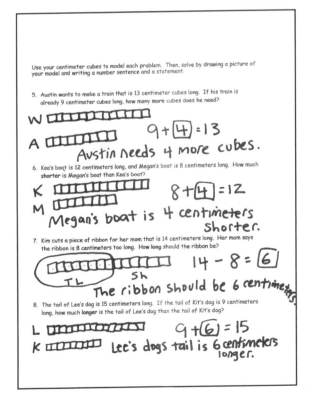

Lesson 9:   Answer *compare with difference unknown* problems about lengths of
                                       two different objects measured in centimeters.   125

© 2015 Great Minds. eureka-math.org
G1-M3-TE-BK3-1.3.1-01.2016

Exit Ticket (3 minutes)

After the Student Debrief, instruct students to complete the Exit Ticket. A review of their work will help with assessing students' understanding of the concepts that were presented in today's lesson and planning more effectively for future lessons. The questions may be read aloud to the students.

Lesson 9:   Answer *compare with difference unknown* problems about lengths of two different objects measured in centimeters.

A

Name _____   Date _____

Number Correct: _____

*Write the missing number.

1.	$17 + 1 = \square$		16.	$11 + 9 = \square$	
2.	$15 + 1 = \square$		17.	$10 + 9 = \square$	
3.	$18 + 1 = \square$		18.	$9 + 9 = \square$	
4.	$15 + 2 = \square$		19.	$7 + 9 = \square$	
5.	$17 + 2 = \square$		20.	$8 + 8 = \square$	
6.	$18 + 2 = \square$		21.	$7 + 8 = \square$	
7.	$15 + 3 = \square$		22.	$8 + 5 = \square$	
8.	$5 + 13 = \square$		23.	$11 + 8 = \square$	
9.	$15 + 2 = \square$		24.	$12 + \square = 17$	
10.	$5 + 12 = \square$		25.	$14 + \square = 17$	
11.	$12 + 4 = \square$		26.	$8 + \square = 17$	
12.	$13 + 4 = \square$		27.	$\square + 7 = 16$	
13.	$3 + 14 = \square$		28.	$\square + 7 = 15$	
14.	$17 + 2 = \square$		29.	$9 + 5 = 10 + \square$	
15.	$12 + 7 = \square$		30.	$7 + 8 = \square + 9$	

EUREKA MATH   Lesson 9:   Answer *compare with difference unknown* problems about lengths of two different objects measured in centimeters.

127

© 2015 Great Minds. eureka-math.org
G1-M3-TE-BK3-1.3.1-01.2016

B

Number Correct: _____

Name _____   Date _____

*Write the missing number.

1.	$14 + 1 = \square$		16.	$11 + 9 = \square$	
2.	$16 + 1 = \square$		17.	$10 + 9 = \square$	
3.	$17 + 1 = \square$		18.	$8 + 9 = \square$	
4.	$11 + 2 = \square$		19.	$9 + 9 = \square$	
5.	$15 + 2 = \square$		20.	$9 + 8 = \square$	
6.	$17 + 2 = \square$		21.	$8 + 8 = \square$	
7.	$15 + 4 = \square$		22.	$8 + 5 = \square$	
8.	$4 + 15 = \square$		23.	$11 + 7 = \square$	
9.	$15 + 3 = \square$		24.	$12 + \square = 18$	
10.	$5 + 13 = \square$		25.	$14 + \square = 18$	
11.	$13 + 4 = \square$		26.	$8 + \square = 18$	
12.	$14 + 4 = \square$		27.	$\square + 5 = 14$	
13.	$4 + 14 = \square$		28.	$\square + 6 = 15$	
14.	$16 + 3 = \square$		29.	$9 + 6 = 10 + \square$	
15.	$13 + 6 = \square$		30.	$6 + 7 = \square + 9$	

   Lesson 9:   Answer *compare with difference unknown* problems about lengths of two different objects measured in centimeters.

EUREKA MATH

Name _____ Date _____

1. Look at the picture below. How much **longer** is Guitar A than Guitar B?

Guitar A is _____ unit(s) **longer** than Guitar B.

2. Measure each object with centimeter cubes.

The blue pen is _____ _____.

The yellow pen is _____ _____.

Lesson 9: Answer *compare with difference unknown* problems about lengths of two different objects measured in centimeters.

129

© 2015 Great Minds. eureka-math.org
G1-M3-TE-BK3-1.3.1-01.2016

3. How much **longer** is the yellow pen than the blue pen?

   The yellow pen is _____ centimeters **longer** than the blue pen.

4. How much **shorter** is the blue pen than the yellow pen?

   The blue pen is _____ centimeters **shorter** than the yellow pen.

Use your centimeter cubes to model each problem. Then, solve by drawing a picture of your model and writing a number sentence and a statement.

5. Austin wants to make a train that is 13 centimeter cubes long. If his train is already 9 centimeter cubes long, how many **more** cubes does he need?

6. Kea's boat is 12 centimeters long, and Megan's boat is 8 centimeters long. How much **shorter** is Megan's boat than Kea's boat?

Lesson 9:   Answer *compare with difference unknown* problems about lengths of
                          two different objects measured in centimeters.

7. Kim cuts a piece of ribbon for her mom that is 14 centimeters long. Her mom says the ribbon is 8 centimeters too long. How **long** should the ribbon be?

8. The tail of Lee's dog is 15 centimeters long. If the tail of Kit's dog is 9 centimeters long, how much **longer** is the tail of Lee's dog than the tail of Kit's dog?

Lesson 9:   Answer *compare with difference unknown* problems about lengths of
two different objects measured in centimeters.

© 2015 Great Minds. eureka-math.org
G1-M3-TE-BK3-1.3.1-01.2016

131

Name _____ Date _____

Use your centimeter cubes to model the problem. Then, draw a picture of your model.

Mona's hair grew 7 centimeters. Claire's hair grew 15 centimeters. How much **less** did Mona's hair grow than Claire's hair?

Lesson 9:   Answer *compare with difference unknown* problems about lengths of
two different objects measured in centimeters.

EUREKA
MATH

Name _____   Date _____

1. Look at the picture below. How much **shorter** is Trophy A than Trophy B?

Trophy A is _____ units **shorter** than Trophy B.

2. Measure each object with centimeter cubes.

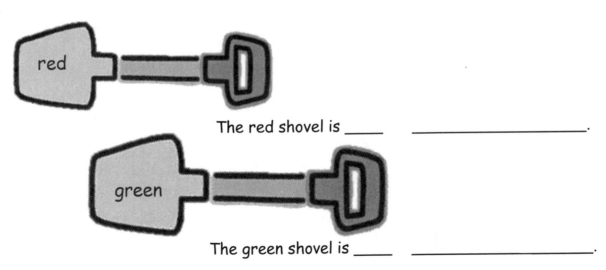

The red shovel is _____   _____.

The green shovel is _____   _____.

3. How much **longer** is the green shovel than the red shovel?

   The green shovel is _____ centimeters **longer** than the red shovel.

Lesson 9:   Answer *compare with difference unknown* problems about lengths of
two different objects measured in centimeters.

133

© 2015 Great Minds. eureka-math.org
G1-M3-TE-BK3-1.3.1-01.2016

Use your centimeter cubes to model each problem. Then, solve by drawing a picture of your model and writing a number sentence and a statement.

4. Susan grew 15 centimeters, and Tyler grew 11 centimeters. How much **more** did Susan grow than Tyler?

5. Bob's straw is 13 centimeters long. If Tom's straw is 6 centimeters long, how much **shorter** is Tom's straw than Bob's straw?

Lesson 9:   Answer *compare with difference unknown* problems about lengths of two different objects measured in centimeters.

© 2015 Great Minds. eureka-math.org
G1-M3-TE-BK3-1.3.1-01.2016

6. A purple card is 8 centimeters long. A red card is 12 centimeters long. How much **longer** is the red card than the purple card?

7. Carl's bean plant grew to be 9 centimeters tall. Dan's bean plant grew to be 14 centimeters tall. How much **taller** is Dan's plant than Carl's plant?

Lesson 9: Answer *compare with difference unknown* problems about lengths of two different objects measured in centimeters.

135

© 2015 Great Minds. eureka-math.org
G1-M3-TE-BK3-1.3.1-01.2016

Mathematics Curriculum

Topic D
Data Interpretation

1.OA.1, 1.MD.4

Focus Standards:	1.OA.1	Use addition and subtraction within 20 to solve word problems involving situations of adding to, taking from, putting together, taking apart, and comparing, with unknowns in all positions, e.g., by using objects, drawings, and equations with a symbol for the unknown number to represent the problem.
	1.MD.4	Organize, represent, and interpret data with up to three categories; ask and answer questions about the total number of data points, how many in each category, and how many more or less are in one category than in another.
Instructional Days:	4	
Coherence Links from:	GK–M3	Comparison of Length, Weight, Capacity, and Numbers to 10
-Links to:	G2–M2	Addition and Subtraction of Length Units
	G2–M7	Problem Solving with Length, Money, and Data

Topic D closes the module as students organize, represent, and interpret personally relevant data in Lesson 10 (**1.MD.4**). As students work as a class to collect, sort, and organize data into a graph, they find great purpose and excitement. They begin to answer, and then ask questions about, the number of data points in a given category and in two categories.

Lesson 11 allows students to take a more independent role in the collecting, sorting, organizing, and representing phases involved in graphing. They work on their own to ask and answer questions about the data set. This work prepares them for the comparison work of the last two lessons.

In Lesson 12, students interpret information presented in graphs by exploring *compare with difference unknown* problems. They begin with visualizing these problems in their easily accessible "equalizing" contexts by answering questions such as, "How many more students would Category A need in order to have the same amount as Category B?" Students use their understanding of comparing lengths from Topics A, B, and C to now compare the responses in three categories.

Lesson 13 continues this exploration with students again interpreting data sets to ask and answer varied word problems including "How many students were polled in all?" and "How many more students are in Category C than in Category A?" (**1.OA.1**). Throughout Topic D, students also apply their learning from earlier in the module as they begin to notice the connection between length units and data points on a graph.

© 2015 Great Minds. eureka-math.org
G1-M3-TE-BK3-1.3.1-01.2016

A Teaching Sequence Toward Mastery of Data Interpretation

Objective 1: Collect, sort, and organize data; then ask and answer questions about the number of data points.
(Lessons 10–11)

Objective 2: Ask and answer varied word problem types about a data set with three categories.
(Lessons 12–13)

Lesson 10

Objective: Collect, sort, and organize data; then ask and answer questions about the number of data points.

Suggested Lesson Structure

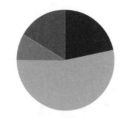

■ Fluency Practice   (13 minutes)
■ Application Problem   (5 minutes)
■ Concept Development   (32 minutes)
■ Student Debrief   (10 minutes)

   Total Time   **(60 minutes)**

Fluency Practice (13 minutes)

- Happy Counting **1.OA.5, 1.NBT.5**   (3 minutes)
- Race and Roll Subtraction **1.OA.6**   (4 minutes)
- Subtraction Within 20 **1.OA.6**   (6 minutes)

Happy Counting (3 minutes)

Note: Practice with counting forward and backward by tens and ones strengthens students' understanding of place value. Counting by twos and fives strengthens addition and subtraction skills.

Repeat the Happy Counting activity from Lesson 2. Choose a counting pattern and range based on the class's skill level. If students are proficient with counting by ones, twos, fives, and tens to 40, start at 40 and go to 80. If they are proficient between 40 and 80, work between 80 and 120. Alternate between counting the regular way and the Say Ten way to reinforce place value.

Race and Roll Subtraction (4 minutes)

Materials: (S) 1 die per pair

Note: This fluency activity reviews the Grade 1 standard of subtracting within 20.

Partners start at 20 and take turns rolling the die to subtract the number rolled from the total. (For example, Partner A rolls 3 and says, "20 – 3 = 17." Partner B rolls 2 and says, "17 – 2 = 15.") They continue rapidly rolling and saying number sentences until they reach 0, which they must hit precisely. Partners stand when they reach 0. Repeat the game as time permits.

Lesson 10:   Collect, sort, and organize data; then ask and answer questions about
              the number of data points.

Subtraction Within 20 (6 minutes)

Materials: (T) enlarged Hide Zero cards (Lesson 2 Fluency Template 1) (S) Personal white board

Note: This review fluency activity helps strengthen students' understanding of the take from ten and take from the ones subtraction strategies, as well as their ability to recognize appropriate strategies based on problem types.

  T: (Show 14 with Hide Zero cards.) How can I take 14 apart to help me subtract?

  S: 10 and 4.

  T: I want to subtract 2 from 14. Write a number sentence to show whether I should subtract 2 from the 4 or the 10.

  S: (Write 4 – 2 = 2.)

  T: Why wouldn't I take from my 10?

  S: You don't need to because you have enough ones.

  T: Yes! It's much easier to just subtract from my ones! Since 4 – 2 = 2, 14 – 2 is …? Write the subtraction sentence.

  S: (Write 14 – 2 = 12.)

  T: (Replace the 4 Hide Zero card with a 2.) Yes!

Repeat with 14 – 5, eliciting the need to take from ten because there are not enough ones. Repeat with similar problems.

Application Problem (5 minutes)

There were 14 items on the table to measure. I already measured 5 of them. How many more items are there to measure?

Note: The use of the word *measure* in this problem raises a level of complexity as students may expect to use a measuring tool to solve. This problem encourages students to consider the context of the whole problem rather than focusing solely on key words.

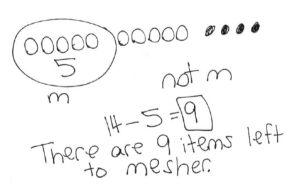

Lesson 10:   Collect, sort, and organize data; then ask and answer questions about the number of data points.

139

© 2015 Great Minds. eureka-math.org
G1-M3-TE-BK3-1.3.1-01.2016

Concept Development (32 minutes)

Materials: (T) 3 pieces of chart paper (S) 1 jumbo craft stick, marker, personal white board

Note: Before today's math lesson begins, prepare three charts:

Chart 1:   *Favorite Read Aloud Books*

Chart 2:   *Favorite Read Aloud Books* with a blank table labeled with *Number of Students*

Chart 3:   *Favorite Sports* with a blank table labeled with *Name of Sport* and *Number of Students*

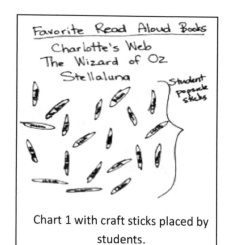

Chart 1 with craft sticks placed by students.

Note: Later in the lesson, students are asked to vote for one of three sports. A topic other than sports can be used to match the class's preference. The lesson requires that only three choices be provided from which students can pick. Model for students that when making a table of information, the symbols within the table all need to be the same.

Have students come to the meeting area with their personal white boards and sit in a semicircle formation.

T: I want to find out which read aloud books you like the most from the ones we have read together. Can you name some of the books we've read?

S: (Name books.)

T: (Choose three titles, and write them on Chart 1. Consider using the most important word from the title to alleviate students from having to write many words during the following activity.)

T: Let's collect some information, or data, to find out how many students like which books the most. How should we collect our data?

S: Ask each student, and then write the names down next to the book title. → Call out each title, and ask us to raise our hands if it is our favorite book.

NOTES ON MULTIPLE MEANS OF REPRESENTATION:

Highlight the critical vocabulary for students while teaching the lesson. Vocabulary to highlight is *collecting, organize, sorting, data,* and *table,* as this is the first time students are being introduced to these words in the context of math. Try relating the vocabulary to something they already know. This is especially helpful to English language learners.

T: Each of you has a craft stick at your table. Decide which book you like the most out of these three choices. Then, write the name of the book on the craft stick. Come up to this chart, and place your stick anywhere on the chart. (Lay the chart on the floor in the middle of the meeting area.)

S: (Label the craft stick, and freely place it on the chart.)

T: Wow, this chart is filled with ____ (the number of students) craft sticks! How many students liked Book A? (Give five seconds for students to count.)

S: (Answers may vary.) I can't count that fast! I need more time.

Lesson 10:   Collect, sort, and organize data; then ask and answer questions about the number of data points.

© 2015 Great Minds. eureka-math.org
G1-M3-TE-BK3-1.3.1-01.2016

T: We have different answers, and some people didn't even get to finish counting! How can we make counting these craft sticks easier?

S: After we count each craft stick, take it off so we can keep track of which ones we have already counted. → Get all the craft sticks for each book, and put them together. We should separate and sort them. → We should organize these sticks by book titles!

T: These are great ideas. I agree! Here is a table. It will help us organize our information or data. (Lay Chart 2 on the floor, and write in the titles. Ask a few student volunteers to rearrange the craft sticks in a horizontal line next to each book title.)

T: Now, is it easier to see?

S: Yes!

T: How can we organize the data so we can count more efficiently and see more easily?

S: Group them by twos. → Group them by fives. Put them in 5-group rows!

T: I love the idea of organizing them into groups of 5. In fact, we are going to arrange some of these sticks in a special way to show groups of 5. Help me count as I show you how this is done.

S: 1, 2, 3, 4, 5. (Count as the teacher points to each craft stick.)

T: Stop! Since we have a group of 5 here, I'm going to take the fifth stick and lay it across the others. (Model.) Show me in the air how this group of 5 is made as we count from 1 through 5 again.

S: 1, 2, 3, 4, 5. (Make tally marks in the air with teacher modeling.)

T: You just used **tally marks**. Tally marks come in groups of 5 where the fifth line always goes across the rest of the four lines. Let's continue with the rest of these sticks.

Students count to 5 and make tally marks in the air as the teacher makes tally marks with craft sticks. After arranging a few craft sticks, ask student volunteers to rearrange the remaining craft sticks.

T: Great job organizing the data by sorting the information we collected. Now we can see and count our information more easily.

Count the tally marks for each book title, and record the number directly on the table. Invite students to interpret the data by posing questions such as those below.

- How many students liked Book A the most?

- How many students liked Book A or Book B the most? (Note: Because the question says *or*, students need to add the number for A and the number for B.)

- Which book is most liked by our classmates? Which book is the least liked of the favorites?

> Favorite Read Aloud Books
>
> | Charlotte's Web | |||| |||| |
> | The Wizard of Oz | |||| || |
> | Stellaluna | |||| |
>
> → Number of Students
> └ Students arrange popsicle sticks, first in rows and then adjust to tally marks.
>
> Chart 2 with craft sticks arranged as tallies.

Repeat the process with favorite sports using football, basketball, and soccer as the three choices. Alternatively, use a theme other than sports if it would have more appeal for the class. Another strategy is to offer *other* as a choice. Students may use the back of the original craft sticks to record their choice. After creating the table on Chart 3, have students write their answers to the following questions:

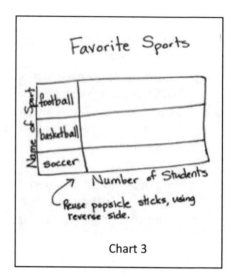

Chart 3

- How many students chose football as the sport they like best?
- How many students chose basketball as the sport they like best?
- How many students chose soccer as the sport they like best?
- What is the total number of students who like soccer or basketball the best?
- Which sport received the most votes?
- Think of a question you could ask a friend about the table.

Note: Save these tables for reference in Lessons 11, 12, and 13 of this topic.

Problem Set (10 minutes)

Students should do their personal best to complete the Problem Set within the allotted 10 minutes. For some classes, it may be appropriate to modify the assignment by specifying which problems they work on first.

Student Debrief (10 minutes)

Lesson Objective: Collect, sort, and organize data, then ask and answer questions about the number of data points.

The Student Debrief is intended to invite reflection and active processing of the total lesson experience.

Invite students to review their solutions for the Problem Set. They should check work by comparing answers with a partner before going over answers as a class. Look for misconceptions or misunderstandings that can be addressed in the Debrief. Guide students in a conversation to debrief the Problem Set and process the lesson.

Any combination of the questions below may be used to lead the discussion.

- How is making a table helpful when we are looking at a lot of information?
- Why is sorting and organizing data important when you are making a table?
- In what ways do tables help us see information in a quicker and easier way?
- Share the problem you made up using the favorite sports table. Solve each other's questions and check your answers.

> **NOTES ON MULTIPLE MEANS OF REPRESENTATION:**
>
> When using a table to answer questions, ask student volunteers to point to the category label to ensure they are referring to the appropriate category. Remind students to also count accurately so that the interpretation of the information displayed in their table is valid.

EUREKA MATH

- How are 5-group rows and tally marks similar? How are they different?
- Why is using **tally marks** better than using 5-group rows when making a table?

Exit Ticket (3 minutes)

After the Student Debrief, instruct students to complete the Exit Ticket. A review of their work will help with assessing students' understanding of the concepts that were presented in today's lesson and planning more effectively for future lessons. The questions may be read aloud to the students.

Name Maria _____   Date _____

A group of people were asked to say their favorite color. Organize the data using tally marks, and answer the questions.

Red	ⅧⅠ
Green	‖
Blue	Ⅷ

1. How many people chose red as their favorite color? __6__ people like red.
2. How many people chose blue as their favorite color? __5__ people like blue.
3. How many people chose green as their favorite color? __2__ people like green.
4. Which color received the least amount of votes? green
5. Write a number sentence that tells the total number of people who were asked their favorite color.
   6 + 5 + 2 = 13

Lesson 10:   Collect, sort, and organize data; then ask and answer questions about the number of data points.

143

© 2015 Great Minds. eureka-math.org
G1-M3-TE-BK3-1.3.1-01.2016

Name _____   Date _____

A group of people were asked to say their favorite color. Organize the data using tally marks, and answer the questions.

green   red   red   blue   red   blue   blue

red   blue   green   blue   red   red

Red	
Green	
Blue	

1. How many people chose red as their favorite color? _____ people like red.

2. How many people chose blue as their favorite color? _____ people like blue.

3. How many people chose green as their favorite color? _____ people like green.

4. Which color received the least amount of votes? _____

5. Write a number sentence that tells the total number of people who were asked their favorite color.

_____

Lesson 10:   Collect, sort, and organize data; then ask and answer questions about the number of data points.

EUREKA
MATH

Name _____   Date _____

A group of students were asked what they ate for lunch. Use the data below to answer the following questions.

Student Lunches

Lunch	Number of Students
sandwich	3
salad	5
pizza	4

1. What is the **total** number of students who ate pizza? _____ student(s)

2. Which lunch was eaten by the **greatest** number of students? _____

3. What is the total number of students who ate pizza or a sandwich?

    _____ student(s)

4. Write an addition sentence for the **total** number of students who were asked what they ate for lunch.

    _____

Lesson 10:   Collect, sort, and organize data; then ask and answer questions about the number of data points.

145

© 2015 Great Minds. eureka-math.org
G1-M3-TE-BK3-1.3.1-01.2016

Name _____   Date _____

Students were asked about their favorite ice cream flavor. Use the data below to answer the questions.

Ice Cream Flavor	Tally Marks	Votes
Chocolate	||||	
Strawberry	|||	
Cookie Dough	⦀⦀ ⦀⦀	

1. Fill in the blanks in the table by writing the number of students who voted for each flavor.

2. How many students chose cookie dough as the flavor they like **best**?

    _____ students

3. What is the total number of students who like chocolate or strawberry the **best**?

    _____ students

4. Which flavor received the **least** amount of votes? _____

5. What is the total number of students who like cookie dough or chocolate the **best**?

    _____ students

6. Which two flavors were liked by a **total** of 7 students?

    _____ and _____

7. Write an addition sentence that shows how many students voted for their favorite ice cream flavor.

    _____

Lesson 10:   Collect, sort, and organize data; then ask and answer questions about the number of data points.

© 2015 Great Minds. eureka-math.org
G1-M3-TE-BK3-1.3.1-01.2016

EUREKA
MATH

Students voted on what they like to read the most. Organize the data using tally marks, and then answer the questions.

comic book	magazine	chapter book	comic book	magazine
chapter book	comic book	comic book	chapter book	chapter book
chapter book	chapter book	magazine	magazine	magazine

What Students Like to Read the Most	Number of Students
Comic Book	
Magazine	
Chapter Book	

8. How many students like to read chapter books the most? _____ students

9. Which item received the **least** amount of votes? _____

10. How many more students like to read chapter books than magazines?

    _____ students

11. What is the total number of students who like to read magazines or chapter books?

    _____ students

12. Which two items did a total of 9 students like to read?

    _____ and _____

13. Write an addition sentence that shows how many students voted.

    _____

Lesson 10:   Collect, sort, and organize data; then ask and answer questions about the number of data points.

147

© 2015 Great Minds. eureka-math.org
G1-M3-TE-BK3-1.3.1-01.2016

Lesson 11

Objective: Collect, sort, and organize data; then ask and answer questions about the number of data points.

Suggested Lesson Structure

- ■ Fluency Practice   (10 minutes)
- ■ Application Problem   (5 minutes)
- ■ Concept Development   (35 minutes)
- ■ Student Debrief   (10 minutes)
   Total Time   **(60 minutes)**

Fluency Practice (10 minutes)

- Sprint: Subtraction Within 20 **1.OA.6**   (10 minutes)

Sprint: Subtraction Within 20 (10 minutes)

Materials: (S) Subtraction Within 20 Sprint

Note: This Sprint addresses the Grade 1 standard of subtracting within 20. This is the second time students are seeing this Sprint. Ask students if they were able to complete more problems than the last time they tried this Sprint.

> **NOTES ON MULTIPLE MEANS OF REPRESENTATION:**
>
> Remember that the strength of the Sprint is in students' on-going experience of success. The tendency is to want to compete with a peer rather than with oneself. At times, it is wise to downplay who improved the most or who got the most correct but rather opt for self-reflection:
>
> - Who feels they tried hard today?
> - Who feels they have improved with their subtraction since the beginning of first grade?
> - Who feels they are memorizing more facts?

Application Problem (5 minutes)

Larry asked his friends whether dogs or cats are smarter. 9 of his friends think dogs are smarter, and 6 think cats are smarter. Make a table to show Larry's data collection. How many friends did he ask?

Note: This Application Problem reviews organizing data, the objective in Lesson 10. Some students may show their work with simple shapes, such as lines or circles, while others may experiment with tally marks.

dogs   O O O O O O O O O

cats   O O O O O O

9 + 6 = 15   9 + 1 = 10
   ⌃   10 + 5 = 15
   15

He asked 15 friends.

Concept Development (35 minutes)

Materials: (T) Chart paper with a table entitled *Favorite Rainy Day Activities* with *Activity* and *Number of Students* on the top line, class list (S) Clipboard, class list (preferably with first names in alphabetical order)

Have students sit in the meeting area in a semicircle formation.

T: (Post the chart.) Let's brainstorm some of our favorite rainy day activities and make a table to see how many students like which activity the best and compare the information. To make this table, what do we need to do first? Turn and talk to your partner.

S: (Answers may vary.) We need to figure out the choices we will vote on.

T: You are right! What are some of your favorite things to do on a rainy day?

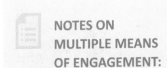

NOTES ON MULTIPLE MEANS OF ENGAGEMENT:

Answers may vary. Choose three activities, and write them down on the chart in the first column. For example, they could be *read a book, watch a movie,* and *play board games.*

Connect literature with the table students will be making in class today. Pick a favorite book that discusses rainy day activities, or alternatively visit with the school librarian to check one out. Read it aloud to the class before making the table to get students ready with ideas.

MP.3

T: Now, what do we do? Turn and talk to your partner.

S: We need to ask around and get everyone to vote.
→ We need to write down who likes which activity the best. → We can use 5-group rows to show our votes.
→ We can use tally marks to show everyone's votes.

T: If we want to compare the information in the table, what do you think is the best way to record the information? Why?

S: (Answers may vary.) 5-group rows help me see better because I can line them up with the other rows. → I like using the tally marks because I can count faster.

T: Good thinking! (Project the class list.) To make sure I interview everyone and get everyone's vote, I'm going to use the class list to help me keep track of who answered my question and what he voted for. (Start from the top of the list. Model collecting data using the class list by asking the first seven to eight students on the list. Check off each name as a student volunteer either makes a tally mark or draws a circle in 5-group rows on the table to represent each vote.)

To save time, call out a choice, and ask the remaining students to raise their hands. Elicit one to two questions to interpret the data. Then, have students come up with additional questions for their partners to answer, including any of the following:

- How many students like to [watch a movie] the most on a rainy day?
- Which rainy day activity is liked the most by our class? The least? How can you tell from the table?
- How many students like to [read a book] or [play board games] the most on a rainy day?
- If two more students voted for [watching a movie], how many students would like [watching a movie] the best?

T: Just like we created this entire table as a class, you will now get to create your own table! Let's look at the Problem Set together to see how!

Lesson 11:   Collect, sort, and organize data; then ask and answer questions about the number of data points.

149

Problem Set (20 minutes)

Students should do their personal best to create questions based on their tables in the Problem Set and answer their partner's questions within the allotted 20 minutes.

Read over the Problem Set directions and go over the steps to follow. Distribute the Problem Set and a class list. Give students approximately 20 minutes to collect and organize their data.

Students who need more structured directions can work in a small group with the teacher for step-by-step guidance.

Photocopy today's Problem Set on two separate sheets of paper so that students can set their papers side by side as they refer to their tables and design questions.

Student Debrief (10 minutes)

Lesson Objective: Collect, sort, and organize data, then ask and answer questions about the number of data points.

The Student Debrief is intended to invite reflection and active processing of the total lesson experience.

Invite students to review their solutions for the Problem Set. They should check work by comparing answers with a partner before going over answers as a class. Look for misconceptions or misunderstandings that can be addressed in the Debrief. Guide students in a conversation to debrief the Problem Set and process the lesson.

Any combination of the questions below may be used to lead the discussion.

- How did you organize your data?
- How could you have used tallies? Pictures? Shapes? What other ways might someone organize data?
- How did you solve Problem 4?
- How did you solve Problem 5? How can you solve Problem 5 by looking at your notes on the class list? Which would be easier to use to find the answer, the class list or the table? Why?
- Look at the Application Problem. How did you organize the data? How did you solve the problem?

Name __Maria__   Date _____

Welcome to Data Day! Follow the directions to **collect** and **organize** data. Then, ask and **answer questions** about the data.

- Choose a question. Circle your choice.
- Pick 3 answer choices.
- Ask your classmates the question and show them the 3 choices. Record the data on a class list.
- Organize the data in the chart below.

Which fruit do you like best?	Which snack do you like best?	What do you like to do on the playground the most?	Which school subject do you like the best?	Which animal would you most like to be?

Answer Choices	Number of Students
monky bars!	⫫⫫⫫ |||
swings!	⫫⫫⫫	
tag!	⫫⫫⫫ ⫫⫫⫫ ||

- Complete the question sentence frames to ask questions about your data.
- Trade papers with a partner, and have your partner answer your questions.

1. How many students liked __monky bars__ the best?

   8 students

2. Which category received the fewest votes? __swings__

   6 students

3. How many more students liked __tag__ than __swings__?

   6 students

4. What is the total number of students that liked __tag__ or __monky bars__ the best?

   20 students

5. How many students answered the question? How do you know?

   26
   I counted the tally marks.

Lesson 11:   Collect, sort, and organize data; then ask and answer questions about the number of data points.

© 2015 Great Minds. eureka-math.org
G1-M3-TE-BK3-1.3.1-01.2016

Exit Ticket (3 minutes)

After the Student Debrief, instruct students to complete the Exit Ticket. A review of their work will help with assessing students' understanding of the concepts that were presented in today's lesson and planning more effectively for future lessons. The questions may be read aloud to the students.

Lesson 11:   Collect, sort, and organize data; then ask and answer questions about
the number of data points.

© 2015 Great Minds. eureka-math.org
G1-M3-TE-BK3-1.3.1-01.2016

151

A

Name _____

Number Correct:

Date _____

*Write the missing number.

1.	17 - 1 = ☐		16.	19 - 9 = ☐	
2.	15 - 1 = ☐		17.	18 - 9 = ☐	
3.	19 - 1 = ☐		18.	11 - 9 = ☐	
4.	15 - 2 = ☐		19.	16 - 5 = ☐	
5.	17 - 2 = ☐		20.	15 - 5 = ☐	
6.	18 - 2 = ☐		21.	14 - 5 = ☐	
7.	18 - 3 = ☐		22.	12 - 5 = ☐	
8.	18 - 5 = ☐		23.	12 - 6 = ☐	
9.	17 - 5 = ☐		24.	14 - ☐ = 11	
10.	19 - 5 = ☐		25.	14 - ☐ = 10	
11.	17 - 7 = ☐		26.	14 - ☐ = 9	
12.	18 - 7 = ☐		27.	15 - ☐ = 9	
13.	19 - 7 = ☐		28.	☐ - 7 = 9	
14	19 - 2 = ☐		29.	19 - 5 = 16 - ☐	
15.	19 - 7 = ☐		30.	15 - 8 = ☐ - 9	

Lesson 11:   Collect, sort, and organize data; then ask and answer questions about the number of data points.

EUREKA MATH

Number Correct: _____

B

Name _____   Date _____

*Write the missing number.

1.	16 - 1 = ☐		16.	19 - 9 = ☐
2.	14 - 1 = ☐		17.	18 - 9 = ☐
3.	18 - 1 = ☐		18.	12 - 9 = ☐
4.	19 -2 = ☐		19.	19 - 8 = ☐
5.	17 - 2 = ☐		20.	18 - 8 = ☐
6.	15 - 2 = ☐		21.	17 - 8 = ☐
7.	15 - 3 = ☐		22.	14 - 5 = ☐
8.	17 - 5 = ☐		23.	13 - 5 = ☐
9.	19 - 5 = ☐		24.	12 - ☐ = 7
10.	16 - 5 = ☐		25.	16 - ☐ = 10
11.	16 - 6 = ☐		26.	16 - ☐ = 9
12.	19 - 6 = ☐		27.	17 - ☐ = 9
13.	17 - 6 = ☐		28.	☐ - 7 = 9
14.	17 - 1 = ☐		29.	19 - 4 = 17 - ☐
15.	17 - 6 = ☐		30.	16 - 8 = ☐ - 9

EUREKA MATH

Lesson 11:   Collect, sort, and organize data; then ask and answer questions about the number of data points.

153

Name _____   Date _____

Welcome to Data Day! Follow the directions to **collect** and **organize** data. Then, **ask** and **answer questions** about the data.

- Choose a question. Circle your choice.
- Pick 3 answer choices.
- Ask your classmates the question, and show them the 3 choices. Record the data on a class list.
- Organize the data in the chart below.

Which fruit do you like best?	Which snack do you like best?	What do you like to do on the playground the most?	Which school subject do you like the best?	Which animal would you most like to be?

Answer Choices	Number of Students

Lesson 11:   Collect, sort, and organize data; then ask and answer questions about the number of data points.

EUREKA MATH®

- Complete the question sentence frames to ask questions about your data.
- Trade papers with a partner, and have your partner answer your questions.

1. How many students liked _____ the best?

2. Which category received the fewest votes? _____

3. How many more students liked _____ than _____?

4. What is the total number of students who liked _____ or

   _____ the best?

5. How many students answered the question? How do you know?

Lesson 11: Collect, sort, and organize data; then ask and answer questions about the number of data points.

© 2015 Great Minds. eureka-math.org
G1-M3-TE-BK3-1.3.1-01.2016

155

Name _____   Date _____

A class collected the information in the chart below. Students asked each other: Among stuffed animals, toy cars, and blocks, which is your favorite toy?

Then, they organized the information in this chart.

Toy	Number of Students
Stuffed Animals	11
Toy Cars	5
Blocks	13

1. How many students chose toy cars? _____

2. How many more students chose blocks than stuffed animals? _____

3. How many students would need to choose toy cars to equal the number of students who chose blocks? _____

Lesson 11:   Collect, sort, and organize data; then ask and answer questions about the number of data points.

© 2015 Great Minds. eureka-math.org
G1-M3-TE-BK3-1.3.1-01.2016

EUREKA
MATH

Name _____ Date _____

Collect information about things you own. Use tally marks or numbers to organize the data in the chart below.

How many **pets** do you have?	How many **toothbrushes** are in your home?	How many **pillows** are in your home?	How many **jars of tomato sauce** are in your home?	How many **picture frames** are in your home?

- Complete the question sentence frames to ask questions about your data.
- Answer your own questions.

1. How many _____ do you have? (Pick the item you have the **most** of.)

2. How many _____ do you have? (Pick the it em you have the **least** of.)

3. **Together**, how many picture frames and pillows do you have?

4. Write and answer two more questions using the data you collected.

   a. _____?

   b. _____?

Lesson 11: Collect, sort, and organize data; then ask and answer questions about the number of data points.

157

Students voted on their favorite type of museum to visit. Each student could only vote once. Answer the questions based on the data in the table.

5. How many students chose art museums? _____ students

6. How many students chose the art museum or the science museum?

    _____ students

7. From this data, can you tell how many students are in this class? Explain your thinking.

EUREKA
MATH®

Lesson 12

Objective: Ask and answer varied word problem types about a data set with three categories.

Suggested Lesson Structure

■ Fluency Practice   (15 minutes)
■ Application Problem   (5 minutes)
■ Concept Development   (30 minutes)
■ Student Debrief   (10 minutes)
   Total Time   **(60 minutes)**

Fluency Practice (15 minutes)

- Addition with Cards **1.OA.6**   (7 minutes)
- Get to 10 or 20 **1.OA.5**   (3 minutes)
- Subtraction with Partners **1.OA.6**   (5 minutes)

Addition with Cards (7 minutes)

Materials: (S) Numeral cards 0–10 (Lesson 2 Fluency Template 2), counters (if needed)

Note: This review fluency activity strengthens students' ability to add within and across ten.

Students sit in partnerships. Students shuffle or mix their numeral cards. Each partner places her deck of cards face down. Each partner flips over two cards and adds her cards together. The partner with the greater total keeps the cards played by both players that round. For example Player A draws 4 and 5 and gives the total 9. Player B draws 9 and 4 and gives the total, 13. Since 9 < 13, Player B keeps the cards. If the sums are equal, the cards are set aside, and the winner of the next round keeps the cards from both rounds. At the end of the game, the players will each be left with 1 card. They each flip their last card over and the player with the highest card says the sum and collects the cards. Students continue to play as time allows.

NOTES ON MULTIPLE MEANS FOR ACTION AND EXPRESSION:

When playing games with students, provide a variety of ways to respond. Oral fluency games should be adjusted for deaf and hearing impaired students. This can be done in many ways including showing the answer with fingers, using personal white boards to write answers, or using a visual signal or vibration.

Lesson 12:   Ask and answer varied word problem types about a data set with three categories.

© 2015 Great Minds. eureka-math.org
G1-M3-TE-BK3-1.3.1-01.2016

159

Get to 10 or 20 (3 minutes)

Materials: (T) 20-bead Rekenrek

Note: Practice with getting to 10 or 20 reinforces strategically counting on, which enables students to solve addition problems by stopping at 10 and continuing to the desired number.

    T: (Show 8 on the Rekenrek.) What number do you see?
    S: 8.
    T: Say the complete number sentence to get to 10.
    S: 8 + 2 = 10.
    T: (Move two beads to make 10.) Good. (Show 18.) What number do you see?
    S: 18.
    T: Say the complete number sentence to get to 20.
    S: 18 + 2 = 20.

Add two beads to confirm, and then continue with other numbers within 20.

Subtraction with Partners (5 minutes)

Materials: (S) Personal white board

Note: This fluency activity reviews subtracting 7, 8, and 9 from teen numbers. Allow students who still require pictorial representations to draw 5-groups to solve.

Assign partners of equal ability. Partners assign each other a number from 11 to 17 (e.g., 12).
On their personal white boards, students write number sentences with 9, 8, and 7 as the subtrahend and solve them (e.g., 12 – 9 = 3, 12 – 8 = 4, 12 – 7 = 5). Partners then exchange personal white boards and check each other's work.

Application Problem (5 minutes)

Kingston's class took a trip to the zoo. He collected data about his favorite African animals. He saw 2 lions, 11 gorillas, and 7 zebras. What might his table look like? Write one question your classmate can answer by looking at the table.

Note: Students may use any of the methods to organize data from the previous lessons. As they are working, circulate and notice how students are representing the data. Encourage them to line up their shapes and focus on organization. Remind students that they need to use the same symbol to represent the information throughout their table. Representations should make counting and comparing data easy. During the Student Debrief, students share and answer their partner's question.

L ||

G   ⊔⊓ ⊔⊓ |

Z   ⊔⊓ ||

How many zebras and gorillas did he see?

Lesson 12:   Ask and answer varied word problem types about a data set with three categories.

© 2015 Great Minds. eureka-math.org
G1-M3-TE-BK3-1.3.1-01.2016

EUREKA
MATH

Concept Development (30 minutes)

Materials: (T) Chart with a three-column vertical graph entitled *Our Favorite Fruits,* chart with measuring rules (Lesson 7) (post on the side of the board), *Favorite Read Aloud Books* chart (Lesson 10) (S) Sticky notes, personal white board

Distribute one sticky note at each student's seat. Have students sit in the meeting area in a semicircle formation.

T: (Post *Our Favorite Fruits* graph.) What are some of your favorite fruits?

S: (Responses may vary. Choose only three, or possibly four, categories from students' suggestions.) Strawberries. → Watermelon. → Apples.

Fill in the three categories as students make suggestions. Have students go back to their seats, write their names on sticky notes, and come back to the meeting area with them.

T: My vote is for strawberry as my favorite fruit. I'm going to place my sticky note right beneath the linewhereit says *Strawberry.* (Model.) Who likes watermelon the best? (Choose a student to come up.) He's also going to place his sticky note right beneath the line where it says *Watermelon.* (Choose another student to come up and place her sticky note for *Apple.* Be sure to have these sticky notes aligned with each other.)

T: We need one more person who likes strawberries the most. (Have student come up.) When he places his sticky note, he's going to put it right beneath my sticky note so there are no gaps or overlap.

T: (Call up one third of the class to post their votes, encouraging them to avoid making gaps or overlaps between the sticky notes.) What do you notice about the rules for completing this chart with our votes on the sticky notes?

S: The rules are just like the rules for measuring! → We had to line up our endpoints when we first started! → We couldn't have any overlaps or gaps. → The sticky notes are the same size, the same length unit.

T: Excellent connections! Let's have the rest of our classmates complete the graph as they put up their votes following these rules.

T: Which fruit is the most popular in our class? Which fruit is the least popular? That means it has the fewest number of votes. How can you tell?

S: I counted. The fruit with the highest total is the most popular. → I just looked at the sticky notes. The longest strip of notes means the most votes. → The shortest strip means the fewest number of votes. → This reminds me of measuring again! The one that used the most length units to measure is the longest one, and that is the most popular fruit!

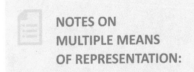

NOTES ON
MULTIPLE MEANS
OF REPRESENTATION:

Students demonstrate a true understanding of math concepts when they can apply them in a variety of situations. Often students learn math concepts in an isolated fashion, and they do not see how to transfer their application to new situations. Celebrate student success when they make these connections.

Lesson 12:   Ask and answer varied word problem types about a data set with three categories.

T: How many students voted for strawberries? Watermelon? Apples? (Record the number amount on the graph.) When we organize our data this way, it makes it easy for us to compare. We call this a **graph**. A graph lets us see the data easily. In this graph, it lines up our data just like when we measure lengths of different items, so we can easily compare.

T: (Point to the corresponding parts of the graph.) Which received more votes, strawberries or watermelon?

S: _____ (category) got more votes.

T: Did you have to look at the numbers for each, or could you see it just by looking at the lengths of the bars made of notes?

S: I just looked at the bar of notes. → The longer bar of notes has more.

T: How many more students would _____ (category) need to have the same amount as _____ (category)? Tell your partner how you figured it out.

S: I just counted the part that was longer, the part that was sticking out. → I used subtraction. → I used addition with a mystery number in the middle. → This reminds me of measuring again! We used all of these strategies when we tried to figure out which length was longer when we compared two things!

T: You are right! So, how many more votes did _____ (category) receive than _____ (category)?

T: (Using the same two categories as above, rephrase the question.) How many *fewer* votes did _____ (category) receive than _____ (category)?

Continue to ask *compare with difference unknown* problems and *put together with total unknown* problems presented by this graph. Ask students to write a number sentence on their personal white boards to show how they reached a solution. If time allows, use the *Favorite Read Aloud Books* chart from Lesson 10 to answer more *compare with difference unknown* problems. Students may work with their partners to answer each other's questions.

Problem Set (10 minutes)

Students should do their personal best to complete the Problem Set within the allotted 10 minutes. For some classes, it may be appropriate to modify the assignment by specifying which problems they work on first.

Lesson 12:   Ask and answer varied word problem types about a data set with
                                  three categories.

© 2015 Great Minds. eureka-math.org
G1-M3-TE-BK3-1.3.1-01.2016

EUREKA
MATH

Student Debrief (10 minutes)

Lesson Objective: Ask and answer varied word problem types about a data set with three categories.

The Student Debrief is intended to invite reflection and active processing of the total lesson experience.

Invite students to review their solutions for the Problem Set. They should check work by comparing answers with a partner before going over answers as a class. Look for misconceptions or misunderstandings that can be addressed in the Debrief. Guide students in a conversation to debrief the Problem Set and process the lesson.

Any combination of the questions below may be used to lead the discussion.

- What are some strategies to figure out how many more or fewer votes a category received compared to the other?

- How are tables and **graphs** similar? How are they different? (Tables and graphs both organize information. With a graph, the information can be compared in a way similar to how length units can be compared.)

- How are the graphs that are used with Problems 3 and 5 different? How are they similar?

- How is measuring objects similar to creating graphs like these to compare information about different categories?

- How does a graph that is created properly help you see and understand information better? Did you follow these rules when you made your graph for Problem 1?

- Look at your Application Problem. What question did you come up with about your table? Share with your partner, and answer each other's question.

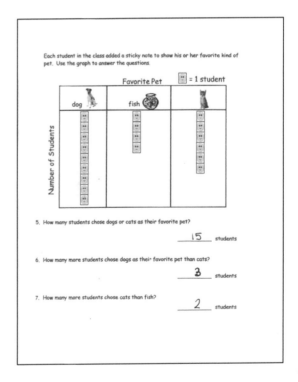

Exit Ticket (3 minutes)

After the Student Debrief, instruct students to complete the Exit Ticket. A review of their work will help with assessing students' understanding of the concepts that were presented in today's lesson and planning more effectively for future lessons. The questions may be read aloud to the students.

Lesson 12:   Ask and answer varied word problem types about a data set with three categories.

163

© 2015 Great Minds. eureka-math.org
G1-M3-TE-BK3-1.3.1-01.2016

Name _____ Date _____

Use squares with no gaps or overlaps to organize the data from the picture. Line up your **squares** carefully.

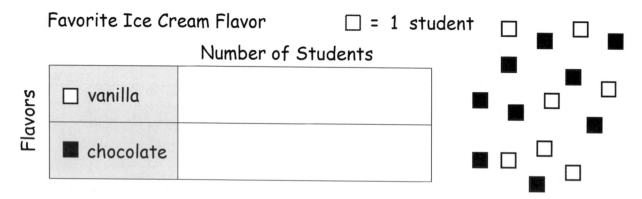

Favorite Ice Cream Flavor   □ = 1 student

1. How many **more** students liked chocolate than liked vanilla? _____ students

2. How many **total** students were asked about their favorite ice cream flavor?

_____ students

Types of Shoe Ties	Ties on Shoes	Number of Students	□ = 1 student
	Velcro		
	laces		
	no ties		

3. Write a number sentence to show how many **total** students were asked about their shoes.

_____

4. Write a number sentence to show how many **fewer** students have Velcro on their shoes than laces.

_____

Lesson 12:   Ask and answer varied word problem types about a data set with three categories.

EUREKA MATH

Each student in the class added a sticky note to show his or her favorite kind of pet. Use the graph to answer the questions.

Favorite Pet   :) = 1 student

dog	fish	cat

Number of Students

5. How many students chose dogs or cats as their favorite pet?

_____ students

6. How many more students chose dogs as their favorite pet than cats?

_____ students

7. How many more students chose cats than fish?

_____ students

Lesson 12:   Ask and answer varied word problem types about a data set with three categories.

165

© 2015 Great Minds. eureka-math.org
G1-M3-TE-BK3-1.3.1-01.2016

Name _____   Date _____

Use squares with no gaps or overlaps to organize the data from the pictures.
Line up your **squares** carefully.

Favorite Animals at the Zoo

	Number of Students
giraffe	
elephant	
lion	

Zoo Animals

Each picture represents 1 student's vote.

1. Write a number sentence to show how many **total** students were asked about their favorite animal at the zoo.

    _____

2. Write a number sentence to show how many **fewer** students like elephants than like giraffes.

    _____

Lesson 12:   Ask and answer varied word problem types about a data set with three categories.

Name _____ Date _____

The class has 18 students. On Friday, 9 students wore sneakers, 6 students wore sandals, and 3 students wore boots. Use squares with no gaps or overlaps to organize the data. Line up your **squares** carefully.

Shoes Worn on Friday   Number of Students   ☐ = 1 student

Shoes	
👟	
🩴	
🥾	

1. How many more students wore sneakers than sandals? _____ students

2. Write a number sentence to tell how many students were asked about their shoes on Friday.

   _____

3. Write a number sentence to show how many fewer students wore boots than sneakers.

   _____

 EUREKA MATH

Lesson 12:   Ask and answer varied word problem types about a data set with three categories.

© 2015 Great Minds. eureka-math.org
G1-M3-TE-BK3-1.3.1-01.2016

167

Our school garden has been growing for two months. The graph below shows the numbers of each vegetable that have been harvested so far.

Vegetables Harvested   [😊] = 1 vegetable

Number of Vegetables

beets

carrots

corn

4. How many total vegetables were harvested?

_____ vegetables

5. Which vegetable has been harvested the most?

_____

6. How many more beets were harvested than corn?

_____ more beets than corn

7. How many more beets would need to be harvested to have the same amount as the number of carrots harvested?

_____

Lesson 12:   Ask and answer varied word problem types about a data set with three categories.

© 2015 Great Minds. eureka-math.org
G1-M3-TE-BK3-1.3.1-01.2016

EUREKA
MATH

Lesson 13

Objective: Ask and answer varied word problem types about a data set with three categories.

Suggested Lesson Structure

■ Fluency Practice   (18 minutes)
■ Application Problem   (5 minutes)
■ Concept Development   (27 minutes)
■ Student Debrief   (10 minutes)
   Total Time   **(60 minutes)**

Fluency Practice (18 minutes)

- Hide Zero Number Sentences **1.NBT.2, 1.NBT.4**   (3 minutes)
- Add Three Numbers **1.OA.2**   (5 minutes)
- Sprint: Add Three Numbers **1.OA.2**   (10 minutes)

Hide Zero Number Sentences (3 minutes)

Materials: (T) Hide Zero cards (Lesson 2 Fluency Template 1)

Note: This fluency activity strengthens the understanding of place value and prepares students for Module 4.

Show students a number from 10 to 40 with Hide Zero cards (e.g., 15). Students say an addition sentence with 10 as an addend (e.g., 10 + 5 = 15). As students say the sentence, pull apart the Hide Zero cards to model the equation. Alternate asking students to say the numbers the Say Ten way and the regular way.

Suggested sequence: 15, 25, 35; 14, 24, 34; and 16, 26, 36.

Add Three Numbers (5 minutes)

Materials: (S) 3 dice per pair, personal white board

Note: This fluency activity reviews adding three numbers.

Assign students partners. Partners take turns rolling the three dice and adding them together. The partner with the higher sum each round scores a point. If there is a tie, players should keep playing until one of them has the higher sum. The person with the higher sum after the tie scores two points. Students record points with tally marks on their personal white boards.

Sprint: Add Three Numbers (10 minutes)

Materials: (S) Add Three Numbers Sprint

Note: This Sprint provides students practice with adding three numbers within 20 and encourages students to apply properties of operations as strategies to add.

Application Problem (5 minutes)

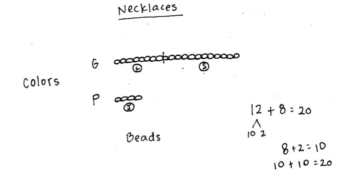

Necklaces

Zoe made friendship necklaces for her 3 closest friends. Make a graph to show the two colors of beads she used. She used 8 green beads for Lily, 4 purple beads for Jamilah, and 12 green beads for Sage. How many green beads did she use?

Note: As students finish, ask additional questions to help them interpret the data, focusing on Grade 1 problem types.

- How many more purple beads would need to be used to have the same amount as the green beads?
- How many fewer green beads does Lily have than Sage?
- If Lily added 3 green beads to her necklace, how many more green beads would she need to have the same amount as Sage?

Concept Development (27 minutes)

Materials: (T) Graph entitled *Favorite Things to Make with Snow* created on easel (data: snow angels—3, snowman—12, and snow forts—2) (S) Personal white board

Note: Adjust the Concept Development as necessary based on observations of student successes and challenges during Lesson 12, as well as during the most recent Application Problems. Today's Concept Development is an opportunity to continue supporting student understanding of the *compare with difference unknown* problem types using appropriate number sentences as they interpret the given data.

Have students gather in the meeting area in a semicircle formation with their personal white boards.

T: (Post the graph.) Here's a graph I made yesterday after talking to the children in my neighborhood. I asked what they like to do in the snow. The graph shows how they answered my question. What do you notice about this graph that is different from the graphs we used yesterday? What is similar?

S: The starting point is on the bottom of this graph. Yesterday, we started from the top. Today, they are built like towers. → But it's still following the rules. → No overlaps. → No gaps. → The same endpoints.

Lesson 13:   Ask and answer varied word problem types about a data set with three categories.

EUREKA MATH

T: Turn and talk to your partner about what you notice. What information can you gather from reading this graph?

Answers may vary. Be sure to record how many votes each category received.

NOTES ON MULTIPLE MEANS OF ACTION AND EXPRESSION:

Asking questions for comprehension during this lesson is important to guide students to evaluate their thinking. This provides students an opportunity to evaluate their process and analyze errors.

T: How many people prefer building a snowman over making snow angels? How did you figure it out?

S: I looked at the snowman and snow angels columns. I counted on from the 4th square in the snowman column since they both have 3 votes. → I already know that there are 3 votes for snow angels and 12 votes for the snowman, so I took away 3 from 12 and got 9.

T: I noticed that yesterday, many students counted to figure out which had more or fewer votes. What subtraction sentence can you use to solve this problem?

S: $12 - 3 = 9$.

T: Explain to your partner how both of these strategies are related.

T: No matter how you solve this, we can use the number sentence $12 - 3 = 9$ as a way to show how we solved the problem.

Continue to ask *compare with difference unknown* and *put together with total unknown* problems, encouraging students to include a number sentence. For all problems, have students discuss how both counting on and using a subtraction sentence are related to one another. Use the following suggested sequence:

- How many more children prefer making the snowman to building a snow fort? Making the snow angel over building a snow fort? Making the snowman or the snow angel?

- How many children took this **poll**? (Note: Students might not be familiar with the word *poll*. Explain that a poll is a situation in which people vote. Give the example that, in this case, students were polled about their favorite things to make with snow.)

In the next set of questions, encourage students to visualize how the graph might change based on the information presented in the following situations:

MP.2

- How many more votes do we need if we want to make the number of votes for building the fort the same as the number of votes for making the snowman?

- Some more children came by and answered the question. If there were 20 children total that answered the question, how many more children came by and voted?

- If 4 more children came along and said they like building snow forts the most, then how many votes would there be for building snow forts?

Use additional sticky notes or tiles for those students who need the concrete–visual support. Again, encourage students to use a number sentence to solve.

EUREKA MATH

Lesson 13:   Ask and answer varied word problem types about a data set with three categories.

171

© 2015 Great Minds. eureka-math.org
G1-M3-TE-BK3-1.3.1-01.2016

Problem Set (10 minutes)

Students should do their personal best to complete the Problem Set within the allotted 10 minutes. For some classes, it may be appropriate to modify the assignment by specifying which problems they work on first.

Student Debrief (10 minutes)

Lesson Objective: Ask and answer varied word problem types about a data set with three categories.

The Student Debrief is intended to invite reflection and active processing of the total lesson experience.

Invite students to review their solutions for the Problem Set. They should check work by comparing answers with a partner before going over answers as a class. Look for misconceptions or misunderstandings that can be addressed in the Debrief. Guide students in a conversation to debrief the Problem Set and process the lesson.

Any combination of the questions below may be used to lead the discussion.

- How is using the counting on strategy related to using a subtraction sentence when looking for how many more or fewer votes one received when comparing two categories?

- How is using the counting on strategy related to using an addition sentence when combining the votes for two or more categories?

- When is it more efficient to use number combinations to solve rather than counting on?

- Look at Problem 1. Which problem on Page 2 connects to this one? How do you know?

- How are the *Favorite Fruit* and *School Day Weather* graphs set up differently?

- Explain to your partner how you solved Problem 9. Compare how each of you solved the problem

- How did the Application Problem connect to today's lesson?

Name Maria   Date

Use the graph to answer the questions. Fill in the blank, and write a number sentence to the right to solve the problem.

School Day Weather   ☐ = 1 day

| sunny ☀ | rainy ☔ | cloudy ☁ |

Number of School Days

1. How many more days were cloudy than sunny?
   1 more day(s) were cloudy than sunny.   5 - 4 = 1

2. How many fewer days were cloudy than rainy?
   2 more day(s) were cloudy than rainy.   7 - 5 = 2

3. How many more days were rainy than sunny?
   3 more day(s) were rainy than sunny.   7 - 4 = 3

4. How many total days did the class keep track of the weather?
   The class kept track of a total of 16 days.   4 + 7 + 5 = 16

5. If the next 3 school days are sunny, how many of the school days will be sunny in all?
   7 days will be sunny.   4 + 3 = 7

Use the graph to answer the questions. Fill in the blank, and write a number sentence that helps you solve the problem.

Favorite Fruit   😊 = 1 student

Number of Students

6. How many fewer students chose bananas than apples?
   1 fewer students chose bananas than apples.   6 - 5 = 1

7. How many more students chose bananas than grapes?
   1 more students chose bananas than grapes.   5 - 4 = 1

8. How many fewer students chose grapes than apples?
   2 fewer students chose grapes than apples.   6 - 4 = 2

9. Some more students answered about their favorite fruits. If the new total number of students who answered is 20, how many more students answered?
   5 more students answered the question.   20 - 15 = 5

Lesson 13: Ask and answer varied word problem types about a data set with three categories.

Exit Ticket (3 minutes)

After the Student Debrief, instruct students to complete the Exit Ticket. A review of their work will help with assessing students' understanding of the concepts that were presented in today's lesson and planning more effectively for future lessons. The questions may be read aloud to the students.

Lesson 13:   Ask and answer varied word problem types about a data set with
three categories.

© 2015 Great Minds. eureka-math.org
G1-M3-TE-BK3-1.3.1-01.2016

173

A

Name _____

Number Correct:

Date _____

*Write the missing number.

1.	$9 + 1 + 3 = \square$		16.	$6 + 3 + 8 = \square$	
2.	$9 + 2 + 1 = \square$		17.	$5 + 9 + 4 = \square$	
3.	$5 + 5 + 3 = \square$		18.	$3 + 12 + 4 =$	
4.	$5 + 2 + 5 = \square$		19.	$3 + 11 + 5 = \square$	
5.	$4 + 5 + 5 = \square$		20.	$5 + 6 + 7 = \square$	
6.	$8 + 2 + 4 = \square$		21.	$2 + 6 + 3 = \square$	
7.	$8 + 3 + 2 = \square$		22.	$3 + 2 + 13 =$	
8.	$12 + 2 + 2 =$		23.	$3 + 13 + 3 =$	
9.	$3 + 3 + 12 =$		24.	$9 + 1 + \square = 14$	
10.	$4 + 4 + 5 = \square$		25.	$8 + 4 + \square =$	
11.	$2 + 15 + 2 =$		26.	$\square + 8 + 6 =$	
12.	$7 + 3 + 3 = \square$		27.	$2 + \square + 7 =$	
13.	$1 + 17 + 1 = \square$		28.	$2 + 2 + \square =$	
14.	$14 + 2 + 2 =$		29.	$19 = 6 + \square +$	
15.	$4 + 12 + 4 =$		30.	$18 = 7 + \square +$	

Lesson 13:   Ask and answer varied word problem types about a data set with three categories.

EUREKA MATH

B

Number Correct:

Name _____   Date _____

*Write the missing number.

1.	$9 + 1 + 2 = \square$		16.	$6 + 3 + 9 = \square$	
2.	$9 + 4 + 1 = \square$		17.	$4 + 9 + 2 = \square$	
3.	$5 + 5 + 1 = \square$		18.	$2 + 12 + 4 = \square$	
4.	$5 + 3 + 5 = \square$		19.	$2 + 11 + 5 = \square$	
5.	$4 + 5 + 5 = \square$		20.	$6 + 6 + 7 = \square$	
6.	$8 + 2 + 2 = \square$		21.	$2 + 6 + 5 = \square$	
7.	$8 + 3 + 2 = \square$		22.	$3 + 3 + 13 = \square$	
8.	$11 + 1 + 1 = \square$		23.	$3 + 14 + 3 = \square$	
9.	$2 + 2 + 14 = \square$		24.	$9 + 1 + \square = 13$	
10.	$4 + 4 + 4 = \square$		25.	$8 + 4 + \square = 15$	
11.	$2 + 13 + 2 = \square$		26.	$\square + 8 + 6 = 18$	
12.	$6 + 3 + 3 = \square$		27.	$2 + \square + 6 = 18$	
13.	$1 + 15 + 1 = \square$		28.	$2 + 5 + \square = 18$	
14.	$15 + 2 + 2 = \square$		29.	$19 = 5 + \square + 9$	
15.	$3 + 14 + 3 = \square$		30.	$19 = 7 + \square + 6$	

EUREKA MATH

Lesson 13: Ask and answer varied word problem types about a data set with three categories.

© 2015 Great Minds. eureka-math.org
G1-M3-TE-BK3-1.3.1-01.2016

Name _____   Date _____

Use the graph to answer the questions. Fill in the blank, and write a number sentence to the right to solve the problem.

School Day Weather   ⬜ = 1 day

sunny ☀	rainy ☔	cloudy ☁

Number of School Days

1. How many more days were cloudy than sunny?

   _____ more day(s) were cloudy than sunny. _____

2. How many fewer days were cloudy than rainy?

   _____ more day(s) were cloudy than rainy. _____

3. How many more days were rainy than sunny?

   _____ more day(s) were rainy than sunny. _____

4. How many total days did the class keep track of the weather?

   The class kept track of a total of _____ days. _____

5. If the next 3 school days are sunny, how many of the school days will be sunny in all?

   _____ days will be sunny.

Lesson 13:   Ask and answer varied word problem types about a data set with three categories.

© 2015 Great Minds. eureka-math.org
G1-M3-TE-BK3-1.3.1-01.2016

Use the graph to answer the questions. Fill in the blank, and write a number sentence that helps you solve the problem.

Favorite Fruit   [image: smiley] = 1 student

Number of Students

6. How many fewer students chose bananas than apples?

_____ fewer students chose bananas than apples. _____

7. How many more students chose bananas than grapes?

_____ more students chose bananas than grapes. _____

8. How many fewer students chose grapes than apples?

_____ fewer students chose grapes than apples. _____

9. Some more students answered about their favorite fruits. If the new total number of students who answered is 20, how many more students answered?

_____ more students answered the question. _____

Lesson 13: Ask and answer varied word problem types about a data set with three categories.

177

Name _____   Date _____

Use the graph to answer the questions.

Animals on Lily's Farm   ☐ = 1 animal

sheep	cows	pigs

Number of Animals

1. How many animals are on Lily's farm in all? _____ animals

2. How many fewer sheep than pigs are on Lily's farm? _____ fewer sheep

3. How many more cows are on Lily's farm than sheep? _____ more cows

    Lesson 13:   Ask and answer varied word problem types about a data set with three categories.

Name _____ Date _____

Use the graph to answer the questions. Fill in the blank, and write a number sentence.

School Lunch Order   [😊] = 1 student

hot lunch	sandwich	salad
😊 😊 😊 😊 😊 😊 😊	😊 😊 😊 😊 😊 😊	😊 😊 😊 😊

1. How many more hot lunch orders were there than sandwich orders?

    There were _____ more hot lunch orders.

    _____

2. How many fewer salad orders were there than hot lunch orders?

    There were _____ fewer salad orders.

    _____

3. If 5 more students order hot lunch, how many hot lunch orders will there be?

    There will be _____ hot lunch orders.

    _____

Lesson 13:   Ask and answer varied word problem types about a data set with
three categories.

179

Use the table to answer the questions. Fill in the blanks, and write a number sentence.

Favorite Type of Book

𝍷𝍷𝍷𝍷 = 5 students

fairy tales	卌 卌 |
science books	卌 |||
poetry books	卌 卌 卌

4. How many more students like fairy tales than science books?

   _____ more students like fairy tales.   _____

5. How many fewer students like science books than poetry books?

   _____ fewer students like science books.   _____

6. How many students picked fairy tales or science books in all?

   _____ students picked fairy tales or science books.   _____

7. How many more students would need to pick science books to have the same number of books as fairy tales?

   _____ more students would need to pick science books. _____

8. If 5 more students show up late and all pick fairy tales, will this be the most popular book? Use a number sentence to show your answer.

   _____

Lesson 13: Ask and answer varied word problem types about a data set with three categories.

© 2015 Great Minds. eureka-math.org
G1-M3-TE-BK3-1.3.1-01.2016

EUREKA
MATH

Name _____   Date _____

1. Each student in the class put a sticky note on the graph to show the vegetable he likes best. Use the graph below to answer the questions. Remember to label your answers.

Vegetables That Students Like Best   ☺ = 1 student

Broccoli	Peas	Carrots
☺ ☺ ☺ ☺ ☺	☺ ☺ ☺ ☺	☺ ☺ ☺ ☺ ☺ ☺ ☺

Number of Students

a. How many students like carrots the best?   _____

b. How many students like carrots and peas the best?   _____

c. How many total students answered the survey?   _____

d. How many more students like broccoli than like peas the best?

_____

e. How many fewer students like broccoli than like carrots the best?

_____

2. Cesar has a piece of string that he wants to use to compare how far his cat's bed

and his dog's bed are from their shared water bowl.

- The string is a lot **longer** than the dog's path to the bowl.

- The string is a lot **shorter** than the cat's path to the bowl.

Whose path is shorter to the water bowl, the dog's or the cat's? Draw a picture to show how you know.

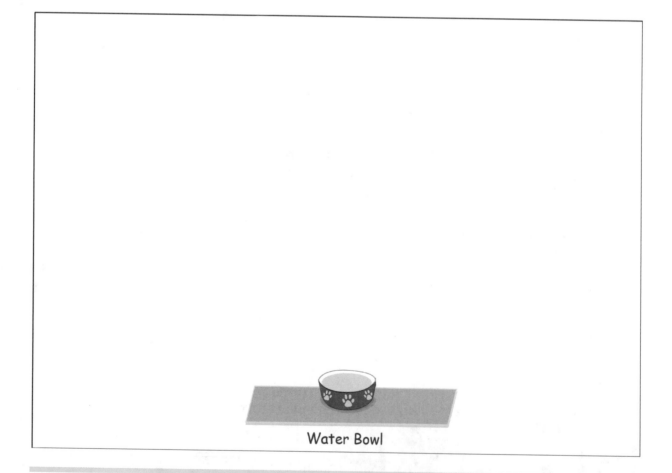

Water Bowl

EUREKA
MATH

3. Circle the pictures that show a correct measurement. [ ] is a centimeter cube.

a.

3 centimeters

b.

4 centimeters

c.

5 centimeters

d.

2 paper clips

e.

3 paper clips

a. Why did you pick these pictures? Explain your thinking with two reasons.

_____

_____

b. What was the length measurement of the **bone** for each correct picture?

_____

c. Why are the measurements for (d) and (e) different?

_____

_____

4. Measure the length of the picture of each item with centimeter cubes.

a.

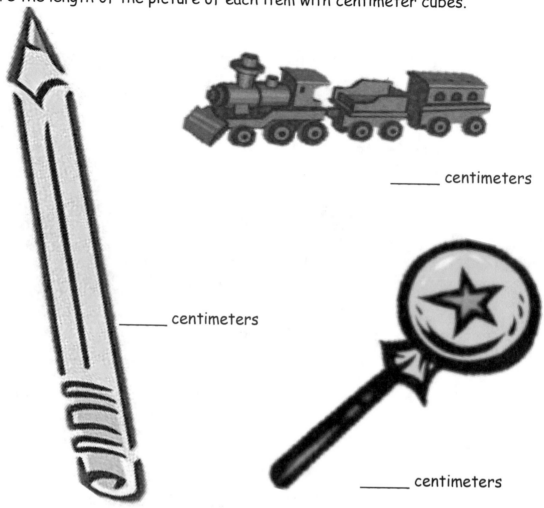

_____ centimeters

_____ centimeters

_____ centimeters

b. Order the train, pencil, and lollipop from shortest to longest.

_____

c. Which item, or items, is longer than the lollipop?

_____

d. How much longer is the pencil than the train?

_____

© 2015 Great Minds. eureka-math.org
G1-M3-TE-BK3-1.3.1-01.2016

| End-of-Module Assessment Task | Topics A–D |
| Standards Addressed | |

Represent and solve problems involving addition and subtraction.

1.OA.1 Use addition and subtraction within 20 to solve word problems involving situations of adding to, taking from, putting together, taking apart, and comparing, with unknowns in all positions, e.g., by using objects, drawings, and equations with a symbol for the unknown number to represent the problem.

Measure lengths indirectly and by iterating length units.

1.MD.1 Order three objects by length; compare the length of two objects indirectly by using a third object.

1.MD.2 Express the length of an object as a whole number of length units, by laying multiple copies of a shorter object (the length unit) end to end; understand that the length measurement of an object is the number of same-size length units that span it with no gaps or overlaps. *Limit to contexts where the object being measured is spanned by a whole number of length units with no gaps or overlaps.*

Represent and interpret data.

1.MD.4 Organize, represent, and interpret data with up to three categories; ask and answer questions about the total number of data points, how many in each category, and how many more or less are in one category than in another.

Evaluating Student Learning Outcomes

A Progression Toward Mastery is provided to describe steps that illuminate the gradually increasing understandings that students develop *on their way to proficiency*. In this chart, this progress is presented from left (Step 1) to right (Step 4). The learning goal for students is to achieve Step 4 mastery. These steps are meant to help teachers and students identify and celebrate what the students CAN do now and what they need to work on next.

A Progression Toward Mastery

Assessment Task Item and Standards Assessed	STEP 1 Little evidence of reasoning without a correct answer. (1 Point)	STEP 2 Evidence of some reasoning without a correct answer. (2 Points)	STEP 3 Evidence of some reasoning with a correct answer or evidence of solid reasoning with an incorrect answer. (3 Points)	STEP 4 Evidence of solid reasoning with a correct answer. (4 Points)
1 **1.MD.4** **1.OA.1**	Student demonstrates little to no understanding of how to read or interpret the graph.	Student demonstrates some understanding of how many students are represented in the graph in a given category or categories (may be off by one or two) but is unable to solve either of the comparison problems accurately.	Student correctly solves (a), (b), and (c) but solves (d) or (e) incorrectly. OR Student solves the comparison problems (d) and (e) correctly but is unable to correctly solve (a), (b), and/or (c).	Student correctly: ▪ Identifies, labels, and solves (a) as 7, (b) as 11, and (c) as 16. ▪ Compares the quantities and writes the difference between the two quantities for questions (d) 1 student and (e) 2 students.
2 **1.MD.1**	Student demonstrates little to no understanding of the comparison.	Student demonstrates some understanding of how the string can be used to compare the two paths (i.e., by using pictures) but provides inaccurate responses.	Student identifies that the dog's path is shorter but is unable to provide a clear explanation. OR Student incorrectly identifies that the cat's path is shorter but is able to draw a picture to explain (this may reflect a linguistic interpretation issue).	Student correctly: ▪ Identifies that the dog's path is shorter. ▪ Explains how the string could be used to compare the distance from each pet's bed to the water bowl (transitivity) by drawing pictures.

Module 3:   Ordering and Comparing Length Measurements as Numbers

EUREKA MATH

© 2015 Great Minds. eureka-math.org
G1-M3-TE-BK3-1.3.1-01.2016

A Progression Toward Mastery				
3 **1.MD.2** **1.OA.1**	Student demonstrates little to no understanding of proper measurement techniques or the reasoning behind them.	Student demonstrates some understanding of proper measurement techniques by either selecting or measuring the correct items but cannot explain her thinking clearly and accurately. OR Student demonstrates some understanding of her thinking behind measurement methods but cannot measure or identify measurements accurately.	Student clearly and accurately completes three out of the four following components: • Identifies (b) and (d) as having the proper measurement. • Cites at least two key elements to measuring accurately (no gaps, no overlaps, attentive to endpoints, same-sized length units) in his own words. • Identifies two correct measurements (2 paper clips and 4 centimeters; units are not required). • Explains that measuring with different lengths of units (small or large paper clips) can result in different quantities of measurement for the same length item.	Student clearly and accurately: • Identifies (b) and (d) as having the proper measurement. • Cites at least two key elements to measuring accurately (no gaps, no overlaps, attentive to endpoints, same-sized length units) in his own words. • Identifies two correct measurements (2 paper clips and 4 centimeters; units are required). • Explains that measuring with different lengths of units (small or large paper clips) can result in different quantities of measurement for the same length item.

A Progression Toward Mastery

4 1.MD.1 1.MD.2 1.OA.1	Student demonstrates little to no understanding of how to measure or use the measurement to compare.	Student demonstrates some understanding of how to measure but is unable to manipulate the measurements to order or compare.	Student accurately measures and orders the items by length but is unable to solve either of the comparison problems. OR Student is able to solve the comparison problems correctly but with slight inaccuracy in the measurements (i.e., off by 1 or 2 centimeters, which then impacts the accuracy of (d)).	Student clearly and accurately: <ul><li>Measures the train (8 cm), pencil (11 cm), and lollipop (9 cm).</li><li>Orders the items by length (train, lollipop, pencil).</li><li>Identifies the pencil as longer than the lollipop.</li><li>Solves the comparison problem correctly by identifying the pencil as 3 centimeters longer than the train.</li></ul>

© 2015 Great Minds. eureka-math.org
G1-M3-TE-BK3-1.3.1-01.2016

Name ___Maria___   Date _____

1. Each student in the class put a sticky note on the graph to show the vegetable he likes best. Use the graph below to answer the questions. Remember to label your answers.

😊 = 1 student

Vegetables That Students Like Best

Broccoli	Peas	Carrots
😊	😊	😊
😊	😊	😊
😊	😊	😊
😊	😊	😊
😊		😊
		😊
		😊

Number of Students

a. How many students like carrots the best?   __7 students__

b. How many students like carrots and peas the best?   __11 students__

c. How many total students answered the survey?   __16 students__

d. How many more students like broccoli than like peas the best?

__1 student__

e. How many fewer students like broccoli than like carrots the best?

__2 students__

2. Cesar has a piece of string that he wants to use to compare how far his cat's bed

and his dog's bed are from their shared water bowl.

- The string is a lot **longer** than the dog's path to the bowl.

- The string is a lot **shorter** than the cat's path to the bowl.

Whose path is shorter to the water bowl, the dog's or the cat's? Draw a picture to show how you know.

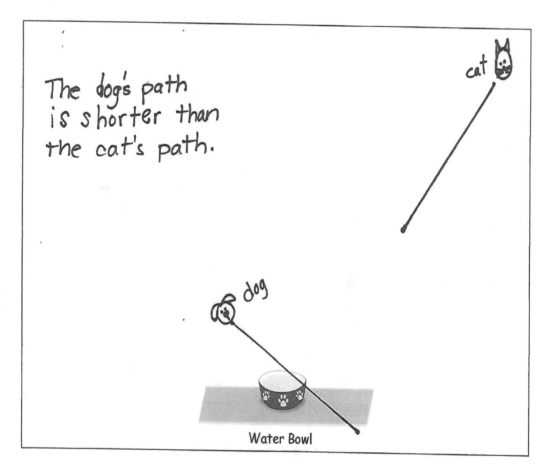

3. Circle the pictures that show a correct measurement. ☐ is a centimeter cube.

(a)

3 centimeters

(b)

4 centimeters

(c)

5 centimeters

(d)

2 paper clips

(e)

3 paper clips

a. Why did you pick these pictures? Explain your thinking with two reasons.

They both start at one end and go to the other end with the same size pieces.

b. What was the length measurement of the **bone** for each correct picture?

4 centimeters   2 paper clips

c. Why are the (d) and (e) measurements with paper clips different?

The paperclips in (e) are different sizes than the paper clips in (d).

4. Measure the length of the picture of each item with centimeter cubes.

a.

_8_ centimeters

_9_ centimeters

_11_ centimeters

b. Order the train, pencil, and lollipop from shortest to longest.

train, lollipop, pencil

c. Which item, or items, are longer than the lollipop?

The pencil is longer than the lollipop.

d. How much longer is the pencil than the train?

The pencil is 3 centimeters longer than the train.

Eureka Math®
Grade 1
Module 3

Special thanks go to the Gordon A. Cain Center and to the Department of Mathematics at Louisiana State University for their support in the development of *Eureka Math*.

Answer Key

GRADE 1 • MODULE 3

Ordering and Comparing Length Measurements as Numbers

Lesson 1

Sprint

Side A

1. 0
2. 10
3. 1
4. 11
5. 2
6. 12
7. 1
8. 11
9. 4
10. 1

11. 11
12. 7
13. 3
14. 13
15. 6
16. 12
17. 11
18. 11
19. 10
20. 4

21. 12
22. 11
23. 7
24. 3
25. 3
26. 5
27. 7
28. 19
29. 2
30. 18

Side B

1. 0
2. 10
3. 1
4. 11
5. 0
6. 10
7. 1
8. 11
9. 3
10. 1

11. 11
12. 6
13. 2
14. 12
15. 4
16. 13
17. 12
18. 12
19. 11
20. 5

21. 13
22. 12
23. 8
24. 2
25. 2
26. 4
27. 6
28. 19
29. 3
30. 18

Problem Set

1. Shorter than
2. Shorter than
3. Shorter than
4. Longer than
5. Shorter than

6. Longer than
7. Shorter than
8. False
9. Answers may vary.

Exit Ticket

Longer than

Homework

1. Peter circled; Peter; Floppy
2. A circled; A; B
3. Shorter than
4. Longer than

5. Longer than
6. Shorter than
7. True
8. Answers may vary.

EUREKA MATH

Lesson 2

Problem Set

1. Longer than; shorter than; longer than
2. a. Longer than
   b. Shorter than
3. Longer
4. Shorter

5. Longer
6. Cup, paper strip, tube
7. Labeled diagram; shorter than
8. Labeled diagram; longer than

Exit Ticket

Labeled diagram; shorter than

Homework

1. The same length as; shorter than; shorter than
2. Shorter than
3. Longer than
4. Shorter
5. Shorter
6. Longer
7. Spoon, cake, paper strip
8. Picture drawn; shorter
9. Picture drawn; taller

Module 3:   Ordering and Comparing Length Measurements as Numbers   **199**

Lesson 3

Sprint

Side A

1.	7	11.	7	21.	19
2.	17	12.	17	22.	12
3.	7	13.	3	23.	16
4.	17	14.	13	24.	6
5.	5	15.	14	25.	19
6.	15	16.	19	26.	5
7.	2	17.	19	27.	19
8.	12	18.	17	28.	19
9.	7	19.	12	29.	2
10.	17	20.	19	30.	9

Side B

1.	6	11.	9	21.	19
2.	16	12.	19	22.	13
3.	6	13.	5	23.	14
4.	16	14.	15	24.	6
5.	5	15.	14	25.	18
6.	15	16.	19	26.	6
7.	1	17.	19	27.	19
8.	11	18.	16	28.	20
9.	9	19.	12	29.	2
10.	19	20.	19	30.	11

EUREKA
MATH

Problem Set

1. The park to the store
2. B
3. A
4. B, C, A
5. 10
6. 12
7. Line drawn on picture showing 8 or 9 blocks
8. Longer
9. Joe
10. Joe's, Caitlyn's, Toby's

Exit Ticket

1. 12
2. Line drawn on picture showing 8, 9, 10, or 11 blocks
3. Longer
4. Answers may vary.

Homework

1. Path between the tree to the flowers
2. B
3. C
4. C, A, B
5. 12
6. 14
7. Line drawn on picture showing 8, 9, 10, or 11 blocks
8. Longer
9. Sal
10. Sal, Jon, Cam

© 2015 Great Minds. eureka-math.org
G1-M3-TE-BK3-1.3.1-01.2016

Lesson 4

Problem Set

1. 3
2. 5
3. 4
4. 5
5. 4
6. 4

7. 3
8. 2
9. 6
10. 3
11. Picture B is circled.
12. Answers may vary.

Exit Ticket

1. 4
2. 4

Homework

1. 4
2. 5
3. 5
4. 7
5. 3

6. 5
7. 3
8. 5
9. 4
10. Picture D is circled.
11. Answers may vary.

EUREKA MATH

© 2015 Great Minds. eureka-math.org
G1-M3-TE-BK3-1.3.1-01.2016

Lesson 5

Sprint

Side A

1.	16	11.	10	21.	9
2.	14	12.	11	22.	7
3.	18	13.	12	23.	6
4.	13	14.	17	24.	3
5.	15	15.	12	25.	4
6.	16	16.	10	26.	5
7.	15	17.	9	27.	6
8.	13	18.	2	28.	16
9.	12	19.	11	29.	2
10.	14	20.	10	30.	16

Side B

1.	15	11.	10	21.	9
2.	13	12.	13	22.	9
3.	17	13.	11	23.	8
4.	17	14.	16	24.	5
5.	15	15.	11	25.	6
6.	13	16.	10	26.	7
7.	12	17.	9	27.	8
8.	12	18.	3	28.	16
9.	14	19.	11	29.	2
10.	11	20.	10	30.	17

Problem Set

1. c. is circled.
2. 3; 3
3. a. 4
   b. 6
   c. 5

4. a. 5
   b. 4
   c. 5
   d. 7
5. Hair clip; marker
6. Longer circled

Exit Ticket

1. 5
2. 4
3. 6
4. 4

Homework

1. a. 13
   b. 5
   c. 15
   d. 8
   e. 10
2. Fire truck, airplane, rowboat

3. a. Rowboat or car
   b. Car; motorcycle, fire truck, or airplane
   c. Fire truck; car, rowboat, or airplane
   d. Car

Lesson 6

Problem Set

1. Caterpillar, fly, bee; 5; 7; 4

2. a. 3
    b. 1
    c. 2
    d. 5
    e. 8
    f. 4
    g. 3

3. 5 cm

4. 8 cm

5. 12 cm

Exit Ticket

1. Wrench, hammer, screwdriver

2. 4

Homework

1. a. 6
    b. 9
    c. 8
    d. 5
    e. 7

2. B, C, A

3. a. D; answers may vary (B, C, or E).
    b. B; answers may vary (A, D, or E).
    c. D
    d. B, C, and E

4. 10 cm

5. 6 cm

Lesson 7

Sprint

Side A

1.	18	11.	16	21.	15
2.	16	12.	17	22.	13
3.	19	13.	17	23.	19
4.	17	14.	19	24.	5
5.	19	15.	19	25.	3
6.	20	16.	20	26.	9
7.	18	17.	19	27.	9
8.	18	18.	18	28.	8
9.	17	19.	16	29.	4
10.	17	20.	16	30.	6

Side B

1.	15	11.	17	21.	16
2.	17	12.	18	22.	13
3.	18	13.	18	23.	18
4.	13	14.	19	24.	6
5.	17	15.	19	25.	4
6.	19	16.	20	26.	10
7.	19	17.	19	27.	9
8.	19	18.	17	28.	9
9.	18	19.	18	29.	5
10.	18	20.	17	30.	4

EUREKA MATH

Problem Set

1. a. 2
   b. 2
   c. 1
   d. 3
   e. 2
   f. 5 or 6 are acceptable
   g. Answers will vary.

2. a. 3
   b. 4
   c. 2
   d. 4
   e. 3
   f. 9
   g. Answers will vary.

Exit Ticket

Answers will vary based on size of paper clips.

Homework

1. a. 4; 6
   b. 3; 4 or 5
   c. 1; 1 or 2
   d. 2; 3
   e. 3; 4 or 5

2. Answers will vary.

Lesson 8

Problem Set

    a.   Answers will vary.

    b.   Answers will vary.

    c.   Answers will vary.

    d.   Answers will vary.

    e.   Answers will vary.

    f.   Answers will vary.

    g.   Answers will vary.

Exit Ticket

Answers will vary.

Homework

1.   a.   Answers will vary.

    b.   Answers will vary.

    c.   Answers will vary.

    d.   Answers will vary.

    e.   Answers will vary.

    f.   Answers will vary.

    g.   Answers will vary.

2.   a.   Answers will vary.

    b.   Answers will vary.

    c.   Answers will vary.

Lesson 9

Sprint

Side A

1.	18	11.	16	21.	15
2.	16	12.	17	22.	13
3.	19	13.	17	23.	19
4.	17	14.	19	24.	5
5.	19	15.	19	25.	3
6.	20	16.	20	26.	9
7.	18	17.	19	27.	9
8.	18	18.	18	28.	8
9.	17	19.	16	29.	4
10.	17	20.	16	30.	6

Side B

1.	15	11.	17	21.	16
2.	17	12.	18	22.	13
3.	18	13.	18	23.	18
4.	13	14.	19	24.	6
5.	17	15.	19	25.	4
6.	19	16.	20	26.	10
7.	19	17.	19	27.	9
8.	19	18.	17	28.	9
9.	18	19.	18	29.	5
10.	18	20.	17	30.	4

Problem Set

1. 1
2. 8 cm; 10 cm
3. 2
4. 2

5. Model drawn; 9 + 4 = 13 or 13 − 9 = 4; 4 cm cubes
6. Model drawn; 8 + 4 = 12 or 12 − 8 = 4; 4 cm
7. Model drawn; 8 + 6 = 14 or 14 − 8 = 6; 6 cm
8. Model drawn; 9 + 6 = 15 or 15 − 9 = 6; 6 cm

Exit Ticket

Model drawn; 8 cm

Homework

1. 1
2. 7 cm; 8 cm
3. 1

4. Model drawn; 11 + 4 = 15 or 15 − 11 = 4; 4 cm
5. Model drawn; 6 + 7 = 13 or 13 − 6 = 7; 7 cm
6. Model drawn; 8 + 4 = 12 or 12 − 8 = 4; 4 cm
7. Model drawn; 9 + 5 = 14 or 14 − 9 = 5; 5 cm

EUREKA MATH

Lesson 10

Problem Set

1. 6
2. 5
3. 2
4. Green
5. 6 + 5 + 2 = 13

Exit Ticket

1. 4
2. Salad
3. 7
4. 3 + 5 + 4 = 12

Homework

1. 4; 3; 10
2. 10
3. 7
4. Strawberry
5. 14
6. Chocolate, strawberry
7. 4 + 3 + 10 = 17

8. 6
9. Comic book
10. 1
11. 11
12. Comic books, magazines
13. 4 + 6 + 5 = 15

Lesson 11

Sprint

Side A

1.	16	11.	10	21.	9
2.	14	12.	11	22.	7
3.	18	13.	12	23.	6
4.	13	14.	17	24.	3
5.	15	15.	12	25.	4
6.	16	16.	10	26.	5
7.	15	17.	9	27.	6
8.	13	18.	2	28.	16
9.	12	19.	11	29.	2
10.	14	20.	10	30.	16

Side B

1.	15	11.	10	21.	9
2.	13	12.	13	22.	9
3.	17	13.	11	23.	8
4.	17	14.	16	24.	5
5.	15	15.	11	25.	6
6.	13	16.	10	26.	7
7.	12	17.	9	27.	8
8.	12	18.	3	28.	16
9.	14	19.	11	29.	2
10.	11	20.	10	30.	17

Module 3: Ordering and Comparing Length Measurements as Numbers

EUREKA MATH

Problem Set

Answers will vary.

Exit Ticket

1. 5
2. 2
3. 8

Homework

1. Answers will vary.
2. Answers will vary.
3. Answers will vary.
4. Answers will vary.

5. 8
6. 14
7. Yes, explanations will vary.

Lesson 12

Problem Set

1. 2
2. 16
3. $5 + 8 + 7 = 20$
4. $8 - 5 = 3$
5. 15
6. 3
7. 2

Exit Ticket

1. $7 + 4 + 3 = 14$
2. $7 - 4 = 3$

Homework

1. 3
2. $9 + 6 + 3 = 18$
3. $9 - 3 = 6$
4. 14
5. Carrots
6. 1
7. 3

EUREKA
MATH

Lesson 13

Sprint

Side A

1.	13	11.	19	21.	11
2.	12	12.	13	22.	18
3.	13	13.	19	23.	19
4.	12	14.	18	24.	4
5.	14	15.	20	25.	4
6.	14	16.	17	26.	5
7.	13	17.	18	27.	9
8.	16	18.	19	28.	14
9.	18	19.	19	29.	4
10.	13	20.	18	30.	5

Side B

1.	12	11.	17	21.	13
2.	14	12.	12	22.	19
3.	11	13.	17	23.	20
4.	13	14.	19	24.	3
5.	14	15.	20	25.	3
6.	12	16.	18	26.	4
7.	13	17.	15	27.	10
8.	13	18.	18	28.	11
9.	18	19.	18	29.	5
10.	12	20.	19	30.	6

© 2015 Great Minds. eureka-math.org
G1-M3-TE-BK3-1.3.1-01.2016

Problem Set

1. $1; 5 - 4 = 1$
2. $2; 7 - 5 = 2$
3. $3; 7 - 4 = 3$
4. $16; 4 + 7 + 5 = 16$
5. $7; 4 + 3 = 7$
6. $1; 6 - 5 = 1$
7. $1; 5 - 4 = 1$
8. $2; 6 - 4 = 2$
9. $5; 20 - 15 = 5$

Exit Ticket

1. 13
2. 1
3. 3

Homework

1. $1; 7 - 6 = 1$
2. $3; 7 - 4 = 3$
3. $12; 7 + 5 = 12$
4. $3; 11 - 8 = 3$
5. $7; 15 - 8 = 7$
6. $19; 11 + 8 = 19$
7. $3; 11 - 8 = 3$
8. Yes; $11 + 5 = 16$

Module 3: Ordering and Comparing Length Measurements as Numbers

EUREKA MATH